Overcome Anxiety

Break Free from Fear, Worry, Trauma, and Negative Thinking

Mark Steinberg, PhD

All Scripture quotations are taken from the Holy Bible, New International Version®, NIV®. Copyright ©1973, 1978, 1984, 2011 by Biblica, Inc.™ Used by permission of Zondervan. All rights reserved worldwide. www.zondervan.com The "NIV" and "New International Version" are trademarks registered in the United States Patent and Trademark Office by Biblica, Inc.™

ISBNs: 979-8-9874856-2-0 (pbk); 979-8-9874856-3-7 (ebook)

Cover and book design by Mayfly Design

Library of Congress Catalog Number: 2023922050
First Printing: 2023
Printed in the United States of America

A single sunbeam is enough to drive away many shadows.

—St. Francis of Assisi

CONTENTS

FOREWORD

Our nation is experiencing a health crisis so pervasive that it is showing up in a decline of life expectancy. We now know this health predicament is rooted in a growing mental health crisis, which can hardly be captured better than by focusing on such an increasingly widespread affliction for which the prevailing remedies are largely unavailing: anxiety. Anxiety is an infirmity that has not been grasped and understood in its full essence. As we chip away at the aspects of anxiety, its medical and psychological manifestations respectively, the need for mind-body integration could hardly be more obvious. The concept had to be explicitly introduced into our discourse, because it wasn't naturally at home within the treating professions.

Such stark partitioning and compartmentalization is not a new problem. Plato recognized it some 2,500 years ago, when he said, "The greatest mistake in the treatment of disease is that there are physicians for the body and physicians for the psyche (ψυχή), although the two cannot be separated."

Going further back, Proverbs 14:30, noted: "A peaceful heart leads to a healthy body."

A peaceful heart was seen as the marker for emotional stability and equanimity, and thus observable for what we would now call the "well-regulated brain." Yet humanity has taken until the twentieth century to discover how to recover such emotional stability and equanimity when it has been deficient or lacking entirely. The process to alleviate the deficiency has been fitful and fraught, and even now largely remains in the hands of pioneers of mental health such as Mark

Steinberg, the author of *Overcome Anxiety: Break Free from Fear, Worry, Trauma, and Negative Thinking*. Dr. Steinberg has been personally willing to breach the traditional boundaries of the practice of psychology and labor at the frontier of this new knowledge base.

What binds the psyche and the soma is our regulatory regime, and we have uncovered the rules by which it operates and developed the means for restoring good regulation. That yogis were demonstrating amazing capacities to control their physiology (blood pressure, heart rate, etc.) just with their meditative techniques should have settled the issue of the mind-body connection. But instead, a controversy raged within the research community for decades as to whether conscious influences could be exerted on the autonomic nervous system, thought to be under essentially "automatic" if not exclusively reflexive control.

Western scientists brought instrumentation to bear on that task, and the field of biofeedback came into existence. By making available measures of physiology that reflected autonomic regulation (e.g., finger temperature, skin sweat gland activity, muscle tension, heart rate, etc.), people could be trained to improve their self-regulatory competence. And perhaps the most compelling finding of all was the new ability to resolve anxiety conditions.

An ability to redress the mental health crisis has arrived none too soon. Anxiety is on a continuum with the fear response, which in turn is rooted in prior traumatic experience. These are physiologically encoded, and thus need to be remediated by means of a physiologically rooted approach, such as neurofeedback. When the functions that are organized to protect us—anxiety, fear, and pain—are severely dysregulated, one has to restore regulatory integrity. One can also disrupt patterns of negative thinking in the moment, and by virtue of the mind-body connection, one can once again appeal to our physiological responses to effect such disruption.

In the big picture, it must be recognized that we are dealing with individual solutions for what are in essence society-level problems. We have to raise our sights and recognize that we have created a society that is profoundly anxiety-producing, if not overtly traumatizing, to many of its inhabitants, from early childhood on up. Perhaps most of all, in this volume, the reader will find satisfaction in the realization that our human predicament is coming to be understood, and it is increasingly subject to our effective management.

Mark Steinberg lights the paths to that end in *Overcome Anxiety*.

—Siegfried Othmer, PhD, chief scientist of EEG Institute,
board chair of Brian Othmer Foundation, and
neurofeedback pioneer with Susan Othmer

INTRODUCTION

The sensation and experience of anxiety is common to everyone. We are all vulnerable to a range of "anxious" feelings, from a mild sense of restlessness, nervousness, or unease to strong feelings of fear, panic, and dread that can be paralyzing.

Although *some* anxiety is a part of normal and unavoidable experience, *excessive and repeated* or *unrelenting* anxiety transcends the floating boundary of normal and tolerable and evolves into a domain where it can become overwhelming, impairing, life-limiting, and destructive to health. This prevalent condition inflicts distress and limitation on millions, so it's no surprise that anxiety drives legions to seek professional help.

As a clinical neuropsychologist, I have treated anxiety, without medication, for four decades. I am quite familiar with the ways anxiety interferes and wreaks havoc in the lives of so many people. In addition to treating patients, I've written extensively about anxiety and its relationship with biological, cognitive, social, and emotional factors that combine to produce symptoms and distress. In this book, I've drawn upon my decades of experience as a clinician on the front lines helping sufferers.

My intention with *Overcome Anxiety* is to simplify the information about how to deal with this problem, how to understand what causes and continues anxiety, and to share realistic expectations about reducing, overcoming, enduring, and conquering this life-debilitating condition. I shine a light on how to get rid of anxiety, as well as how to live adaptively with anxiety even when it cannot be entirely eliminated.

The subtitle, *Break Free From Fear, Worry, Trauma, and Negative Thinking*, describes some hallmarks of anxiety syndromes and refers to the hopeful potential for escaping the shackles of anxiety. Living without the encumbrance of overwhelming anxiety is doable—I have helped and witnessed thousands of sufferers do so over my decades of clinical practice.

Those of us who profess to know about or help mitigate anxiety offer opinions, treatments, claims, and opinions about how to get rid of it. I have no intention of bombarding readers with more techniques or promises that may be "helpful" (or otherwise) but do not make substantial positive impact upon dealing with this problem. I share and report actual facts and provide encouragement, practicality, and science that I have had the greatest success with consistently over many years in quelling the anxiety that has disrupted the lives of thousands of my own patients.

My approach in *Overcome Anxiety* offers verified, scientifically proven interventions that do not simply mask symptoms, nor do they depend on deep abstract analyses of purported causes or "reframing" anxiety through cognitive exercises or distraction. Any realistic approach to dealing with anxiety must recognize (despite good success achieved and without pejorative assessments of an "anxious character") that anxiety is a part of life, and adjustments, recurrences, adaptations, and mitigations may be the best that can be done for many people at a given time and over a period of time. When applied correctly, this suffices for even the most severely plagued.

While much can be done to alleviate anxiety, we should be realistic about guiding those who have limited success in reducing their problem, and we should not categorize them as having an impaired and lifelong defect that can, at best, be only partially mollified with repeated interventions.

We must address anxiety sufferers with understanding, compassion, and viable treatments to overcome anxiety. At the same time, we must be realistic about validating and enjoining those whose anxiety struggles endure and may have limited positive response to interventions.

Overcome Anxiety sheds light on getting rid of anxiety, as well as living with it when it cannot be entirely eliminated.

Whether you become anxious periodically in response to certain situations or people, or suffer regularly from mental, emotional, and physiological symptoms—excessive anxiety, intrusive thinking, or obsessive worrying may be detracting from your health, functioning, and life satisfaction.

You are not alone, though you may feel that way when you sense you're not in control of your mind and body. The good news is that you can overcome anxiety so that life's provocations and challenges don't take you down and make you miserable.

Millions of people have found ways to reduce, contain, or eliminate anxiety without reliance on harmful substances or habits. You can, too.

PART I

THE REALITY
OF ANXIETY

CHAPTER 1

Prevalence and Impact

Anxiety can manifest in a variety of symptoms: obsessive worry, intrusive thoughts, negativity, and physiological symptoms—fight-or-flight responses such as rapid heartbeat, chest tightness, staggered breathing, and the extremely frightening onset of panic attacks. Excessive and persistent anxiety often accompanies or can lead to depression, sleep disorders, addictions, and/or poor concentration.

As human mammals, we have nervous systems designed to interact with our environments and other people in ways that engage in purposeful behavior, goal attainment, and sense and protect ourselves from danger and harm. To this end, we are wired with fight-or-flight mechanisms that activate in response to many stimuli within and outside ourselves. We react to threats that are *actual* and/or *perceived*. Since life is complicated and often ambiguous, our brain and nervous system may often overreact, "just in case." The cost of erring on the side of caution includes accelerated nervous system responses that may linger. This is experienced as anxiety

However, it is also wise to realize and accept that many people are vulnerable and prone to the intrusion of anxiety despite significant reduction of symptoms and remarkable gains in well-being. The majority of people have, at some stressful period, fallen victim to the throes of great anxiety, accompanied by self-doubt and questions about their normality.

Let this *cat out of the bag*: you can be—and probably are—mostly normal, despite forays into the thickets of overwhelming and crushing distress. Millions who suffer periodic anxiety bouts recover and resume normal functioning. Although such experiences "under the gun" can be extremely unpleasant, they instill sensitivity and compassion for those who struggle mightily over even longer periods.

Because many others suffer with enduring anxiety and battle to keep from succumbing to its debilitating effects and despair, I consider it important to validate these struggles and to avoid "pie-in-the-sky" promises or aspirations to eliminate anxiety entirely. Life is not pain-free, physically or emotionally. Though a great deal can be done to live without anxiety: acknowledging the necessity of tolerating some anxiety—minimizing it substantially, and learning to live more happily with what won't go away is prudent and reasonable—a premise that is a foundation of this book.

In my experience as a veteran neuropsychologist, the mainstream approaches to treating anxiety promoted (along with the underlying attitudes most professionals hold) are underpinned by certain philosophies of what causes anxiety and what can be done about it. A reductionist medical view of anxiety is that it arises from a biochemical imbalance in the brain and nervous system, influenced by many factors including genetics, circumstances, lifestyles, and traumas. Though I agree with this basic premise, I am not persuaded by the mainstream medical "solution" of prescribing *anxiolytics* (medicines that reduce anxiety biochemically), especially *de rigueur* and as a sole treatment. In this standard medical approach, the symptoms are treated as needed without respect to the cause of the anxiety (in order to vanquish it). The side effects (including addiction) are ignored, or medicines are switched or new ones added, and the patient is left to weigh the costs and benefits.

The more psychological or psychodynamic view is that some people have "anxious personalities," and the best that can be done is to help the patient "manage" this lifelong problem by keeping it under wraps through cognitive therapy, interpersonal support, and perhaps with the aid of medications. In my view—buttressed by decades of experience successfully eliminating anxiety—this low bar of expectation and opinion is the result of inadequate treatment methods and a poor understanding of people, biology, and the nature of anxiety.

Nonetheless, the reality is that significant portions of populations across most cultures do tend to have brains, constitutions, and nervous systems that predispose them to anxiety. Thus, even when they are able to ward off the intrusive and debilitating effects of anxiety, they may repeatedly succumb to old ways: episodes of acute or extended battles with fear, panic, obsessive worry, negativity, etc. We need to understand and treat this as a function of physiology, rather than will or character defects.

A fair appraisal of and approach to overcoming anxiety must include methods that work without deleterious side effects, are practical and accessible, and respect the idea that many people can overcome anxiety to a great degree—such that their lives are vastly improved and happier—but they may not, once and for all, entirely eliminate anxiety from their lives and minds.

Anxiety Is Everywhere

The National Institute of Mental Health reported a Harvard Medical School estimate that 31.1 percent of adults in the US experience an anxiety disorder at some point in their lives.[1] Only a fraction of those people will seek treatment. In addition to those diagnosed with an anxiety disorder by professionals, millions suffer privately with symptoms on a continuum ranging from mild to severely debilitating.

Anxiety problems can be chronic, transient, or recurring. They can vary in intensity and the degree of impact they make on a person's functioning and sense of well-being. Individual sensitivities vary greatly, as do abilities to tolerate anxiety, perceptions of distress, responses and coping mechanisms.

Anxiety is not a unitary entity, but rather occurs on a continuum of heightened nervous system response. Some people struggle with constant or intermittent anxiety symptoms (including irritability, worry, obsessive or intrusive thinking, etc.). Some get spontaneous panic

---

1. Harvard Medical School, 2007. National Comorbidity Survey (NCS). (2017, August 21). https://www.nimh.nih.gov/health/statistics/any-anxiety-disorder*

attacks; and others experience predictable and marked fear reactions to known stimuli or events (phobias).

Anxiety manifests itself in various symptoms that may form allied disorders that become maintained or stimulated by underlying anxiety: sleep disorders, addictions, and poor concentration, to name a few.

As human mammals, we have nervous systems designed to interact with our environments and other people in ways that engage in purposeful behavior, varying levels of attachment and detachment, goal attainment, and to sense and protect ourselves from danger and harm. To this end, we are wired with fight-or-flight mechanisms that activate in response to many stimuli within and outside ourselves. We react to threats that are *actual* and/or *perceived*. Since life is complicated and often ambiguous, our brain and nervous system may often overreact, *just in case*. The cost of erring on the side of caution includes accelerated nervous system response that may linger. This is experienced as anxiety.

Since anxiety is multifaceted and not static, describing a continuum doesn't yield accuracy or clear parameters for understanding or action. Distress is in the eye (brain) of the beholder. However, let's establish that *some* anxiety is a part of normal and unavoidable experience, whereas *excessive and repeated* or *unrelenting* anxiety transcends the floating boundary of normal and tolerable into a domain where it becomes overwhelming, impairing, life-limiting, and destructive to health.

Anxiety Chameleons

Most people recognize anxiety by overt symptoms, such as "feeling" anxious, overwrought, or scared, with or without specific cause. The heightened arousal, fight-or-flight response, revved up sensation (possibly with rapid heartbeat or staggered breathing) are frequent anxiety hallmarks. Often a person experiences racing or intrusive thoughts. Anxiety assumes many guises, and symptoms vary and change depending upon the individual and differing circumstances and provocations.

People who suffer with phobias are acutely and consciously aware of what makes them anxious. Phobias may be specific and predictable (heights, bugs, public speaking, enclosed spaces, driving, flying, etc.). In these cases, avoidance of the feared stimulus reduces anxiety. Or someone may be focused on fear of the unknown, such as health problems, the future, or the possibility of losing a loved one.

However, anxiety masquerades and manifests in other behaviors, feelings, and conditions. Difficulty concentrating or sleeping are often due to anxiety. Racing or intrusive thoughts indicate anxiety. Oversensitivity, irritability, and extended aggression are also signs of an anxious nervous system.

Addictions always involve anxiety problems, as the addictive cycle features the use of substances or behaviors to reduce anxiety, followed by withdrawal that spikes the craving and need to indulge again. The person in the throes of withdrawal or craving may experience intensely uncomfortable feelings and obsessive needs, but anxiety is at the foundation. Any viable method of treating addictions must address anxiety, as well as other complicating factors.

Other Manifestations

For different reasons and in varying degrees and circumstances, people avoid and procrastinate. When such behaviors become chronic, excessive, and debilitating, the driving force is undoubtedly the overwhelming anxiety that motivates avoidance or escape.

Avoidance is a common way of trying to cope with anxiety. Maintaining absence or distance from anxiety-provoking situations temporarily reduces anxiety, but worries and fears have a way of intruding and taking over thoughts and feelings. Avoidance also brings eventual consequences and inevitably restricts activities and lifestyles.

Procrastination is another manifestation of anxiety. Though it becomes a habit, procrastination evolves from avoidance due to fear and anxiety over making decisions: the numerous sequential decisions needed to identify the parameters of tasks and initiate some steady conscious decision-making necessary in the process of getting things done.

Some people react to anxiety by becoming irritable, aggressive, or paranoid. The world seems out to get them. The brain clams up, becomes suspicious and defensive, and may become impervious to reason, evidence (or lack thereof), or attempts at reassurance or de-escalation.

Suffice it to say that for many millions of people, anxiety is a way of life, chipping away at health, happiness, productivity, and basic functionality. From worrying tendencies to panic attacks to disrupted sleep and relationships, anxiety is a stubborn demon that haunts and disrupts when the brain and nervous system fail to maintain self-regulation and control.

Hope and the Company You Keep

The prevalence of anxiety creates difficulties and barriers for millions of people. Chances are that you interact with many people who have trouble with anxiety. Even if *you* have things mostly under control, anxiety sufferers in your midst or circle of relationships can affect you due to their neediness, insecurity, and appeals for support or reassurance. Anxiety can also become "contagious" in the sense that a highly anxious or fearful person projects jitteriness and drama into communal situations. Thus, someone else's anxiety can impose itself upon you.

As you read this book, you will recognize experiences and truths familiar to you and those you interact with and care about. Despite its prevalence and commonality, anxiety can be reduced and often eliminated from surfacing to the point of interference and major distress. You can take the lead in assuming better control of yourself and illuminating the way for those who suffer intense anxiety to heal and flourish.

CHAPTER 2

Sympathy, Indifference, and Disbelief

Anxiety sufferers know all too well how those not plagued with this affliction have a very hard time understanding what the experience feels like. Everyone has known periods of feeling anxious, nervous, or fearful, but the feelings are different for those afflicted with chronic, recurrent, and persistent anxiety. To awaken from sleep beset with symptoms such as panic, mind racing, rapid heartbeat, and feeling fearful and hyperalert for no known reason doesn't make sense, yet it happens again and again.

The day may begin with dread: tension and vigilance wracking body and mind, racing thoughts, imaginary demons, and palpable fear of what might ensue in the coming hours. Gripping anxiety may subside, only to return predictably in cycles. Some people rely on medications, without which life becomes unbearable. Unfortunately, drugs provide only temporary relief, are habit-forming, have side effects, and often stop working.

Besides feeling inner anguish and terror, anxiety sufferers worry about the reactions of others to their distress. In an effort to hide or cover up their anxiety, they may try to create a mask of calmer composure, or suppress the raging angst inside. They may be unable to conceal the distressing symptoms. Between a rock and a hard place, they must face the world with debilitating anxiety or withdraw from it by avoiding activities that induce or spike more anxiety.

Either way is upsetting—like the old quip:

Q: What's worse than finding a worm in your apple? (i.e., Experiencing great personal distress?)

A: Finding half a worm! (i.e., Discovering that people notice your anxiety and/or minimize or dismiss your suffering.)

When stressed with anxiety, sufferers face three types of responses from others: sympathy, indifference, or disbelief.

Sympathy

Though you are not alone in struggling with anxiety, it feels lonely and isolating when "the bull is goring you." Having close, trusted confidants and a support system can be indispensable. You may have sympathetic family members, friends, or professionals to lean on and confide in when you are under duress. Though not a cure for the anxiety, people who are sympathetic and on whom you can rely and trust may bring needed comfort and partial relief. Your confidants may have experience with significant anxiety themselves, or they may be sympathetic to your plight, have an emotional attachment to you, and an investment in your wellness.

Sharing your trepidation and discomfort with those who show understanding can decrease stress and allow you to feel more accepted. Even in more formal public situations, gentle acknowledgment of anxiety can ease the burden and relieve some of the stress of having to hold it in, pretend, or put on a smile or stoic face.

Truly, we may reasonably expect others to sympathize with pain, because everyone experiences pain in one form or another. However, with the pain of chronic or severe anxiety is often less relatable and harder to identify with.

Having others sympathize with your anxiety can be reassuring and soothing, if only for the palliative effects of acceptance and temporary assuagement. Even though receiving sympathy for your distress is not the solution, it surpasses other less-personable reactions.

Indifference

The opposite of caring might well be indifference. We all need and want attention. Though the lack of attention and caring may heighten anxiety, people do not become anxious on purpose to get attention. Such behavior would backfire anyway, as the anxiety persists and expresses itself despite the negative attention it may incur.

Though people with anxiety usually prefer to divert attention from their discomfort, the lack of acknowledgment from others about one's internal storm can seem insensitive, dismissive, or rejecting. Paradoxically, though you don't want others to emphasize anxiety by noticing it, you likely feel perplexed by how can they act as if everything is fine and okay when you are is such obvious distress.

The reality is that most people are preoccupied with thoughts about themselves. They may have their own levels of distress, but are less (if at all) concerned with anyone else's overwhelming problems. Like a catch-22: on the one hand, you want people to recognize and understand your misery; on the other hand, you don't want your distress to stand out conspicuously.

Indifference can be alienating; but it's better than untoward or insensitive reactions of disbelief.

Disbelief

To the chagrin of anxiety sufferers, much of the world does not have a clue about how overwhelming and disabling anxiety can be. Whereas cancer or a broken leg readily evokes sympathy, anxiety is a "hidden" affliction. Those without the problem may think that sufferers are too sensitive, exaggerating, or even weak or lacking in character. This unfair judgment is not only callous, but far from the reality of inner turmoil. Nonetheless, insensitive or dismissive reactions and attitudes are devastating to anxiety sufferers—adding insult to injury.

In some perverse twist of reasoning (and perhaps some prideful and defensive justification of their own struggles), observers who minimize the impact of anxiety may think that anxiety is not an obstacle sufficient to inhibit or keep people from doing what they want, ought, or have to do. Their tough stance is that you should just "get over it."

Unhelpful Reactions

Whereas uncaring or dismissive people virtually ignore or downplay the anxiety in others, many individuals (especially those in relationship with the anxious person) try to help by various means of response or support. They ask if there's anything they can do to help. They may attempt to provide reassurance (e.g., "It's gonna be okay." "There's nothing to worry about." "Please try to calm down.")

Comforters might offer distractions, medicine, intoxicants, or food in attempts to soothe the anxious person. If appropriate and welcomed, physical touch, simple proximity, or accompaniment by someone trusted may temporarily appease the overexcited sufferer.

In extreme situations or cases—such as intense panic attacks—the victim might need permission or assistance to quickly leave the immediate environment. All too often, the anxiety onset is so intense that a hospital emergency visit ends up being the recourse. Panic attacks can feel like heart attacks to the uninitiated. Many such hospital emergency visits resolve with an anxiolytic (anxiety medication) administered along with the expensive tests to rule out life-threatening events. The poor sufferer is left to sheepishly hear that "it's just anxiety."

Because anxiety disorders tend to be tenacious and repetitive, those trying to be supportive or having to deal on a regular basis with the difficulties of others' anxiety tend to vacillate between sympathetic assistance and alternate exasperation. Continuing anxiety frustrates the sufferer and those trying to aid. Helpers often become impatient, and this may be expressed tacitly through body language or overtly with demands or "constructive" criticism. Though understandable, such vacillation on the part of supporters can seem quite confusing and harsh to the person who is anxious and dependent. Revealing vulnerability and need requires trust. When trust is thwarted by frustrated reactions, the anxious person is left feeling even more overwhelmed and alone. Again, the "rock and hard place" quandary for both parties: the overly anxious and those trying to provide support.

Where to Turn

Anxiety is prevalent, frequently confusing, and illogical, and draws mixed reactions from those surrounding the sufferer. Such pervasive and intangible qualities elicit conflicting views and mixed attitudes, often unsympathetic or minimally tolerant. Despite its ubiquity, anxiety sufferers face limited and restrictive options on managing or resolving their problems.

In the coming chapters, I will explain what causes anxiety and its various manifestations (including fears, worry, obsessive thinking, trauma, and addiction), the limited mainstream options typically offered for its treatment, and current very effective treatments for relief.

I will complement and support my views with evidence, as well as offer some spiritual perspectives that have been most helpful to me and so many others in resolving inner turmoil and growing to determine what is changeable and to accept the limits on what we may want to achieve and relieve, but fall short.

Next, we review interventions that are typically available to anxiety patients, and how the mental health system treats the disorder and those whom it afflicts.

CHAPTER 3

What Causes Anxiety

What causes anxiety in the first place?

The sensation and experience of anxiety is common to all people. The experience originates in the survival mechanisms of mammalian nervous systems and is also noted in the behavior and physiology of all animals.

In assessing the causes of anxiety, we may find a chicken-and-egg cycle of origination and consequence that depends on where we focus upon the intrusion. Do the thoughts cause the anxiety, or does the anxiety generate the thoughts? Most people attribute their anxiety to persistent disturbing thoughts. When anxiety is preponderant, it can stimulate the recurrence of upsetting thoughts. As the thoughts and feelings perpetuate each other, the cycle can be confusing, overwhelming, and seemingly mysterious. Though thoughts and feelings can be mutually reinforcing, I submit that the *feelings* (generated by neurological brain responses) are primarily responsible for anxiety and the ensuing thoughts are the mind's attempts to explain, interpret, and predict the outcomes of what the body is physiologically undergoing.

Anxiety responses include a variety of neurological, sensory, cognitive, and emotional experiences and reactions to events and/or perceptions that appear threatening, dangerous, or uncomfortable. The causes of anxiety may be detected, labeled, and analyzed according to what triggers our physiological, perceptual, or sensory responses, and can be measured by objective means and/or subjective experiences and descriptions.

The human fear response is unquestionably accepted as natural, often appropriate, and instrumental for self-protection and survival. However, every person knows and has experienced anxiety that has occurred in response to events and ideas that the logical mind may deem unworthy of overly anxious responses. Those whose lives are overrun with anxiety commonly feel the onset of anxiety with no discernible or predictive trigger, they simply experience a sudden and overwhelming internal reaction, seemingly unrelated to the circumstance during which it occurs.

Anxiety/Fear: There Is Danger

Anxiety, fear, and their many manifestations and symptoms underlie much of human behavior. We can never fully get rid of these intense emotions, nor ought not completely dissolve them, for they are fundamentally hardwired and basic to survival.

The problem for so many is that anxiety and fear overflow and flood subjective unpleasant feelings fueled by an overreaction of fight-or-flight physiological response. When the nervous system jumps into this high alert, the conscious mind constructs a narrative that matches the internal panic.

In response to danger or threat (actual or perceived) the brain formulates a story to interpret the drama of the body's automatic response and match it with circumstances. Therein the case of a palpable danger or threat, the body and brain need to gear up for action, protection and defense, and readiness for any "just in case" mode. This survival response is appropriate and useful when actual threat and internal response coincide.

However, far too often, the brain and nervous system react *as if* there is substantial threat, even in the clear absence of such. It's a potential that is projected, rehearsed, and experienced as if it were happening in the present. This real time fear response is commonly experienced in various symptoms like phobias, worries, self-consciousness, intrusive thoughts, and social or performance anxiety. People afflicted with these habitual negative emotions *know* they are anxious. They do what they can to lessen the anxiety or avoid the provoking stimulus.

Just as troubling and more ubiquitous is the unconscious influence of fear and anxiety in everyday responses to life problems, challenges, and ordinary activities. If one has a suspicious nature, a history of being taken advantage of, or general trust issues, these will undoubtedly overshadow a fair interpretation of the motivations and actions of others.

Psychological and material insecurity will color perceptions and decisions and often override conscious awareness of their influence. When trying to end a disagreement or dispel inner negative expectations, the effects of past trauma often sway our reactions with influences beyond conscious awareness. It's hard to be impartial or to evaluate and plan judiciously with a pounding heart and fearful forecast.

Anxiety Triggers

Many people afflicted with anxiety can pinpoint or predict the triggers. Phobias, stress, environmental demands (social situations, new situations, public speaking presentations, and meetings), and worries about life's uncertainties are among the "demons" that shadow and lurk to spring upon the vulnerable.

Anxiety can also be triggered by the body's response to physiological imbalances, such as low blood sugar, dehydration, hunger, reactions to foods or medications, or withdrawal from self-medicating substances. As stated, the perception of danger or threat (real or imagined) invokes nervous system overarousal, producing any number of manifestations of fight-or-flight reaction: accelerated heart rate, difficulty breathing, sweating, racing thoughts, narrowing of focus, muscle tightness, hypervigilance, general panic, insomnia, etc.

Although we can surmise that many people are prone to anxiety disorders by genetic predisposition, the development of an anxiety disorder to the extent of life interference happens over time as the person develops habitual brain habits that coalesce into repeated physiological responses. The basic problem of habitual and excessive anxiety responses comprises cause-and-effect cycles of behavioral attempts to escape the fraught anxiety reactions through self-medication (or prescribed medications), compulsive or ritualistic behaviors, obsessive rumination, overindulgence, and other diversions and palliative efforts.

For people with phobias, the actual stimulus, or even the thought or anticipation of the feared event or situation, triggers perturbed *thought fields* as well as cognitive and physiological anxiety responses.

Many people incur dramatic anxiety responses when ingesting or exposed to foods or substances that are "toxic" in the neurological energy sense. The classic meaning of toxicity is akin to poisonous, implying that a toxic substance can be lethal and rapid neutralization is necessary. We often hear certain people or relationships described as "toxic" or "bad" for us. Neither meaning depicts the toxic effects cited in regard to the neurological energy situation. Although the malaise-inducing effects of certain foods, smells, chemicals, or other environmental influences are commonly accepted (especially by very sensitive people), most people (including health professionals) are unaware of the causative influence of person-sensitive substances on reliably inducing anxiety. Several decades of treating people with anxiety and other emotional disorders have empirically verified for me, my patients, and other highly trained practitioners the direct effects and correlations between the ingestion of certain foods, supplements, or the use of particular self-care products and the onset or recurrence of anxiety. This finding is scientifically demonstrable and empirically validated.

Though these reactions may not be detected medically as allergies, a significant percentage of the population has food and other sensitivities. Whereas some people verify through experience that certain foods disagree with them (usually through digestive or skin reactions), most are unaware of the direct causal connection between their reactions to toxins and the emanation of pronounced anxiety.

Traumas

Whether consciously realized or not, traumas induce anxiety. We all suffer traumas; some are major and many are seemingly minor, but nonetheless pile up our stress load, wear down our resilience, and reduce our thresholds for anxiety.

Throughout my professional experience, I've clearly observed that unresolved trauma continues in the emotional brain and lurks to precipitate and sustain anxiety. Though often unrecognized as such, experiences and perceptions in daily life can trigger emotional memories that subject the brain to physiological responses of heightened arousal and defense as though the originating threat is live and present.

Different sources of common challenges and provocative experience can trigger anxiety; but underlying traumas can associate past experiences and exacerbate the brain's response to perceived threat. A trauma (physical, environmental, or emotional) precipitates an involuntary emotional and physiological response to what the nervous system regards as dangerous or threating.

A trauma may result from the following:

1. An injury caused by an extrinsic agent, especially one causing a disturbance in normal functioning.

2. A psychological shock or severe distress from experiencing a disastrous event outside the range of usual experience, such as rape or military combat.

3. A psychological shock or severe distress from experiencing an attack or loss, or a manipulation or taking advantage of one's vulnerability.

4. A disordered psychological or behavioral state resulting from severe mental or emotional stress or physical injury.

5. A violation or a *perceived violation* of a person's familiar ideas about the world and their rights.

The traditional concept of trauma is predicated on an assumption of a catastrophic event outside the range of usual experience. However, trauma encompasses a much broader range of causal situations and is a very common occurrence. Traumas are *universal*; they occur intermittently in everyone's life. Recovering from traumas is necessary for basic physical functioning and mental and emotional health, and can be accomplished routinely by most people (given the right tools, training, and support).

In order to understand these points, we must start with the assumption that *we all have vulnerabilities.* Vulnerabilities make us physically and psychologically prone to attack and to breakdown from life's events and forces.

As we accumulate experiences and get to know ourselves, we can ideally identify (and often protect ourselves) against many of our own vulnerabilities. Certain vulnerabilities are genetically coded and specific. Vulnerabilities are the weak links that allow us to become ill or dysfunctional in a myriad of ways. For example, we know that particular diseases tend to run in families. A family history of heart disease, diabetes, depression, etc., doesn't determine that we will be afflicted with these conditions, but it does weigh the odds that put us at greater statistical risk.

Trauma occurs when we are caught in an "attack" on one of our "weak links," whether the attack was intentional, random, or even *imagined*. The essence of trauma is that it penetrates defenses, seizes upon vulnerability, and leaves us feeling hurt, defenseless, and usually causes us to "relive" in some way the embedded traumatic experience. Common sense observation and our own experiences will confirm this cause and effect link.

As an example, consider this common experience:

After a vehicle accident or near-accident, many people habitually tend to tense up when reminders or even vaguely similar conditions present themselves, as if girding up for another accident. For example, suppose you were in an auto accident that really rattled you, perhaps even injured you. For a long time afterward, you might become anxious when approaching the scene of that accident. Or say the police were pursuing a speeding car that blew through a red light and almost hit your car. Subsequently, you might panic whenever you hear the sound of a police siren in the distance while you are driving. This reaction evokes both physiological (fight-or-flight) and psychological / mental / emotional responses. The set of defensive responses to an anticipated offending event (in the absence of its presence or direct evidence that it will necessarily occur) is called *perseveration*: responding to an event that is no longer present.

Many forms of trauma can occur when people are subjected to harsh conditions, abuse, overwhelming negativity, rejection, racism, isolation, poverty, and so forth. But for many people, even having to deal with the more mundane traumas that result from the daily interactions, demands, and conflicts typically associated with *ordinary* relationships can be overwhelming.

When your spouse, boss, friend, child, relative, partner, teammate, or peer does not react in the way you want or expect, it can be emotionally traumatic. You need not be oversensitive or even know that the trauma is occurring. You can, however, tell by the aftereffects.

Remember: the nature of trauma is that it causes us to relive or anticipate an event or reaction that previously left us hurt, shocked, exposed, or defenseless. So when you find yourself (or your relationship partner) revisiting the same conflicts, scripts, and (quickly accelerated) emotional responses to the faintest of cues, you will know that a trauma has been incited and activated.

For these traumas, you don't need access to an emergency room or years of therapy. What you do need is the realization that you are probably reacting to some provocation that stimulates a less-than-conscious, unresolved emotional vulnerability that initiated a trauma. Such awareness will enable you to see your inner responses and your outward behavior as reactions to a trauma that you may perceive viscerally as necessary, but which are neither a function of choice and clear thinking, nor conducive to planning, keen observation, evaluation, or problem-solving.

Self-Regulation

People afflicted with chronic anxiety typically suffer from inefficient or impaired *self-regulation*. Our bodies and brains have native mechanisms to run the internal "housekeeping." This includes the maintenance of appropriate and contained fight-or-flight responses, self-soothing mechanisms, alertness and relaxation, inhibits for overreactions and overarousal, and smooth transitions between "states" of arousal, including waking to sleeping.

Disruptions in or faulty development of good self-regulation easily results in anxiety. This is the body's way of indicating something is not right inside with neuronal transmission and regulation. As will be explained further, an elegant and enduring solution to this problem is the establishment and honing of self-regulation, most notably through neurofeedback brain training. The establishment and practice of structure, healthy and regular sleep, exercise, and eating habits are also necessary and effective in promoting self-regulation and diminishing anxiety.

Contrary to popular belief, and the assertions of many mental health professionals, it is not our cognitive thoughts that cause anxiety—although they may accompany, reinforce, and harmonize with the physiological anxiety already overextended. Our physiological and visceral responses come first, habitually triggering the mind's *narrative* to explain, interpret, and justify the anxious experience.

Because of this cause-and-effect origin, therapies based upon cognitive reframing (or teaching people to reinterpret and minimize or contextualize their thoughts) are misguided and largely ineffective in controlling and eliminating anxiety.

Since anxiety originates physiologically (and the thoughts are accompaniments), reducing anxiety must begin with quelling the *origin* of the physiological cause. Trying to modify feelings through logic is backward: like putting on your shoes first and then your socks!

States and Speeds

The self-regulation mechanisms native to our biology involve complex and intricate neurological firing mechanisms that allow the brain to transition among *states* and maintain a homeostatic balance. *State* refers the level of arousal, awareness, and accompanying sensations and perceptions induced by the mechanisms of neurological transmission. Measurements, including frequency, amplitude, phase (and other scientific calibrations), can record and reflect the body/brain's physiological and sensate experience of different states, or levels of consciousness and awareness.

Brain nerve transmissions collude at different "speeds." In fact, our brains have tens of thousands of speeds of nerve firings. One way to think about this is by comparing it to the different speeds at which moving vehicles operate.

Varying Brain Speeds

Brain neurons fire neurologically at different speeds. These neural transmissions are measured in physics terminology, such as frequency, amplitude, phase, coherence, etc. The speed and morphological (structure of the EEG formations) mechanisms determine the varying states of the brain. Think of "state" as a condition of arousal that influences wakefulness, mood, perception, satiety, desire, and motivation. Biologically, we shift through different states on a constant basis. Some are subtle, and some are dramatic. The transition from waking to sleeping is an obviously marked shift in state from conscious to unconscious.

A car has different speeds (measured in miles per hour). In order to drive safely, comfortably, and fluidly, we must be able to navigate at different speeds, according to the changing road conditions and traffic. We must not get locked into one or several favorite or habitual speeds. Similarly, our brain has to shift speeds fluidly, as appropriate for the conditions and needs. This includes a natural and automatic shifting down from alert waking states into unconscious sleep states.

Our brain knows how to do this and has been doing so since birth. However, for many reasons, as mentioned, brains can easily fall into maladaptive habits whereby the shifting speed mechanisms become dysregulated. The brain "forgets" how to access and shift among speeds (neurological transmissions) conducive to varying conditions and necessary states.

For example, we are wired to shift on a daily basis into sleep states. Waking states may be compared to driving on streets or freeways (with many alternating miles per hour necessary to drive safely and comfortably), whereas sleeping states may be likened to inching along at slower speeds. People who have trouble falling or staying asleep (tens of millions!) have disrupted brain patterns that do not shift regularly and/or efficiently among the speeds that guide them in and out of restorative sleep. This of course, is accompanied by anxiety. A perpetuating cycle can develop whereby trouble sleeping creates physiological weariness and anxiety, often triggering latent worry about not falling asleep which, unfortunately, further interferes with sleep.

Thought Fields

We can understand anxiety as a natural mammalian response to actual or perceived threat or the sensation or expectation of exposure or danger. Basically, anxiety is a physiological response that propels the nervous system into a fight-or-flight state. This reaction is complicated by the conscious mind's perception of high alert and the conditioned response of the cognitive mind to explain, interpret, or justify the automatic neurological reaction.

People who experience high anxiety associate this uncomfortable feeling with distressing thoughts, images, or memories. Indeed, the thoughts and feelings become intertwined, usually in such a way that the anxious person believes that the thoughts are causing the anxiety. This is not quite true. As I explained earlier, cognitive thoughts are not what cause anxiety (although they may accompany, reinforce, and harmonize with the physiological anxiety). The physiological and visceral response comes first, habitually triggering the mind's *narrative* to explain, interpret, and justify the anxious experience.

The interconnection between visceral neurological/emotional states and thoughts that accompany them constructs a *negative thought field*. Such formations tend to keep the connections bound together, almost like a chemical reaction. This state tends to be stable. When it endures, the negative thought field binds the negative emotion (anxiety) regardless of its origination.

Though the term *thought field* seems like an abstract concept, thought fields can be measured physiologically, subjectively, and empirically. Fortunately, negative thought fields, once identified, can be eliminated by a very effective treatment called Thought Field Therapy (TFT). This treatment will be explained in subsequent chapters. For now, as we identify the causes of anxiety, it's relevant to introduce the concept of negative thought fields as causative of intense anxiety. Treatment with Thought Field Therapy, or its advanced version called Voice Technology, collapses the structure of negative thought fields by eliminating the *perturbations* (disruptions in the energy flow) that bind the negative thoughts and feelings, thus rapidly eliminating the distress.

When the negative thought fields are eliminated, the result is a complete absence of the previously (just before treatment) of anxiety, trauma, and other negative emotions. In some cases, one or a few treatments result in the prolonged absence of the treated negative emotions. In such cases, (often with phobias), we can accurately conclude that the disturbance has been *cured*. Of course, persisting and chronic anxiety is more complicated and requires a broader understanding and approach. Such a broader understanding and approach can be found in Thought Field Therapy (TFT)

From Causes to Effects and Solutions

From this chapter, we move on to the manifestations of anxiety, effects upon habits and lifestyles, and about processes and potential for relieving it.

CHAPTER 4

Mental Health Interfaces and Treatments

Anxiety is such a fundamental and pervasive problem that it takes front and center stage in mental health interventions. The symptoms, and ensuing label of *anxiety*, are usually prominent. Yet there may be other presenting and overriding symptoms such as depression, mania, behavioral disturbances, intrusive or bizarre thinking, hallucinations or delusions, obsessive-compulsive behaviors, phobias, sleeplessness, etc., that are always accompanied (if not caused) by anxiety.

The focus of intervention may address specific and/or various symptoms, but efficacy must address (and calm) the "runaway train" of an overexcited and dysregulated nervous system.

The professional mainstream prioritizes treatment by recommending and prescribing medications. This conventional approach relies on the idea that anxiety is physiologically based. Inherent in the medication route are these assumptions:

✓ The "biochemical imbalance" (neurotransmitter role) in anxiety must be treated by chemicals.

✓ The patient will likely need to take medications for a long time to control anxiety.

✓ The basic problem—biochemical imbalance—cannot be adequately or fully corrected without medication(s).

✓ Adjunct treatments (various therapies) can be helpful, but cannot solve the basic anxiety problem that requires medication.

Interestingly (and ironically), physicians who recommend prescription drugs to quell anxiety may also recommend psychotherapy in conjunction with the medications. Such "lip service" regarding the helpful role of psychotherapy belies a flawed pretense: if the anxiety problem is truly biological (and requires medication), then what does psychotherapy actually add? Alternatively, if psychotherapy is effective and critical, then why is there a need for medication?

In my experience, many physicians don't put much stock in psychotherapy, but will acknowledge or patronize the role of therapy. They often espouse the traditional belief that medication is necessary and effective and, since medical doctors are at the head of the healthcare hierarchy, they can influence and prescribe for patients without divulging their doubts or considerations about "talk" therapy or other diverse and less-conventional approaches.

I have distinct opinions and mixed feelings about the traditional medical approach of treating mental health problems with medications. On the one hand, I, too, firmly believe that mental health problems are physiologically based, though I know there are far more effective and safer methods to successfully treat the physiological problem. So I concur scientifically with the medical community on the biological basis and the need for biological intervention, just not with drugs, to treat mental health.

On the other hand, I sympathize with the proclivity of physicians to be dismissive or condescending about therapy, because I have found (from four decades in the field) most psychotherapy is ineffective in treating anxiety disorders.

Perhaps my most trenchant objection to the pharmaceutical method for treating anxiety and other mental issues is that this solution (medication) usurps actual control from the individual and typically leads to dependence, side effects, and reduced efficacy.

There are appropriate places for psychotropic medications in the treatment of crises and severe mental illness; I am not stridently against their use. However, the pervasive prescribing and overwhelming acceptance of psychotropics as the main (and typically *only*) treatment method for anxiety and other disorders produces limited efficacy and carries significant risks.

Given the reality of the pervasive prescription route and the constrained knowledge and resources for adequately treating anxiety, sorting out what anxiety sufferers face when seeking relief is useful.

Seeking Help

By the time someone seeks help, anxiety is significantly interfering with functioning and well-being. It may have reached crisis proportions.

Despite this discomfiting motivation, reaching out takes great courage. The plea for help often entails embarrassment, fear, confusion, and doubts. When someone seeks professional assistance for the first time, the foray is shrouded by uncertainty and vague expectations. *How will I be treated? Will it hurt or expose me? How soon can I expect relief?* These are some of the unspoken hesitations of the uninitiated.

Anxiety veterans seeking help may have a more jaded outlook. Their previous encounters with treatment have likely been less than satisfying or effective. Treatment and environments vary from benign and futile (i.e., a lousy therapist) to harsh or restrictive (e.g., unpleasant side effects of medications, perhaps even involuntary hospitalization).

Thus the initiative (or coercion) for treatment is fraught with marginal chances of successful outcomes. Yet the anxiety sufferer reaches out and soldiers on in the hopeful (and even desperate) search for relief. The attitudes toward professionals are often ambiguous and hesitant.

I am sadly reminded of the lamentable story of the guy complaining about his dentist to a friend.

"When he's working on my teeth, I always experience such pain. I hate going there!"

The consoling friend suggests, "Have you tried discussing your concerns with the dentist?"

"Heck no," says the patient, "I may have to go back again for treatment!" Nonetheless, anxiety can be so painful and disruptive that sufferers brave what comes in the quest for relief.

Venues For Help

Physicians

Typically, the initial outreach is to a physician: a family doctor or perhaps a psychiatrist. The contact or visit may occur in conjunction with another medical problem (e.g., sleep, heart irregularities, pain, etc.), or it may be a straightforward complaint about anxiety (or panic, depression, unpleasant thoughts, etc.).

Most physicians are poorly trained to deal with anxiety and other mental health issues. They are trained to prescribe medications, and are quick to do so. Using the standard medical differential diagnosis method, if they cannot find a physical reason for the symptom distressing the patient, they will diagnose anxiety. Often, the patient self-diagnoses anxiety, and the physician concurs and follows with a prescription.

Rarely is the patient sufficiently informed of the potential side effects or the habit-forming risks of such medications. In general, patients are not encouraged to ask multiple questions about their condition or treatment recommendations, as the physician is short on time and *patience*, and eager to see the waiting *patients*.

Therapists

Anxiety sufferers may also seek help from some type of therapist. This may be a psychologist, licensed counselor, social worker, hypnotist, or other providers holding themselves out to the public for mental health treatment.

An increasing number of online resources offer counseling-type services. Such services are typically some variety of "canned" or systematized version of talk therapy, offering support and/or specializing in types of clients or problems (e.g., LBGTQ, couples, teens, etc.) The appeal of these services is convenience, privacy, and lower cost.

Many traditional and experienced therapists in private practice have converted to online sessions as a main mode of "seeing" patients. Even so, it is curiously difficult for people seeking help to get an appointment. The COVID pandemic launched the proliferation of virtual therapies that has persisted and grown even as the shutdown subsided. Rather than augment in-person visits, therapists increasingly seem to prefer this remote mode, despite many disadvantages.

Even so, appointments are hard to come by. HMO insurance companies offer extremely restricted access to mental health services. Their waiting lists are usually months long, and appointments after the initial one are parsed out few and far between. The HMO approach favors medication, group sessions, and very brief counseling. Patients are expected to "get better" quickly (as if a brief course of antibiotics will suffice and end their care seeking).

Large HMO conglomerates (such as Kaiser and Sutter Health in California) have long waiting lists (months), limited appointments, and restricted services (usually only talk therapy). In typical HMO fashion, their employees can only spend short amounts of time with patients, have burdensome caseloads, and are discouraged from (or sanctioned for) offering innovative therapies.

Over the years—just for the heck of it—I have inquired about providing much-needed mental health treatment to these large healthcare companies overflowing with untreated patients seeking care. Without exception, I've been told that they are not accepting new in-network or contract mental health providers. And yet their own providers are overworked, limited, and frustrated, while patients wait and cannot gain access.[2]

Hospitals

I doubt that many people enjoy being in hospitals. Though hospitals provide much needed care (often lifesaving), patients are usually in acute pain, if not chronic illness. Care is expensive, often impersonal (despite the caring and sacrificing efforts of doctors and other healthcare professionals), and staffing shortages have become routine. The

---

2. In my (thankfully) thriving practice, I give new and existing patients appointments typically within one week.

stressful hospital experience is perhaps maximized when the stay is for mental health issues.

Patients may end up in the ER on a voluntary or involuntary basis. Patients experiencing panic attacks, particularly for the first time, can become so overwhelmed and frightened that they think they're dying or having a heart attack. They wait in the ER, heart pounding, fearful and confused, wondering if they will survive. When they are finally seen, the diagnosis of anxiety is rendered with an impassive and unsympathetic dismissal as anxiety. Usually, they are given an anxiolytic (anti-anxiety medication) at the ER and advised to follow through with their physician and/or a therapist. Calmer from the short-acting medication and perhaps feeling a bit sheepish, they leave the revolving door, fearing and expecting their anxiety to return, only to wonder what else to do.

Patients who experience severe mental health crises, suicidal ideation or attempts, aggressive acting out, bizarre thinking or behavior, often end up in some form of inpatient custody: the so-called mental health ward. These locked facilities may vary in patient stays from a day to several weeks. The mental health patient may enter voluntarily (usually escorted by family members) or may be committed involuntarily.[3] Though involuntary commitment on an incident-related basis is typically limited to seventy-two hours or less, it may be extended depending on patient behavior and diagnoses.

Stints in a locked mental health ward can be unpleasant and traumatic. Some patients are highly agitated or even paranoid; and they are resentful, rebellious, and/or aggressive until subdued by powerful medications (usually antipsychotics). Such incarcerations are often desperate last resorts and may serve to contain the patient and prevent incipient or further harm. Ironically, this crude intervention may serve to "teach" the defiant or recalcitrant patient that "this is what happens when you are consistently uncooperative." Although aversive and even punitive, involuntary stays may have the effect of influencing

---

3. In California, such involuntary commitment is known as a 5150; 5150 is the number of the section of the Welfare and Institutions Code, which allows an adult who is experiencing a mental health crisis to be involuntarily detained for a seventy-two-hour psychiatric hospitalization when evaluated to be a danger to others, or to one's self, or is gravely disabled.

the patient to engage in needed (and previously avoided) treatment. Nonetheless, hospitals are a rough ride for overly distressed and sensitive patients.

Mental health crises and issues cover a broad swath. Often, these patients have involved mental health needs that range from distressing and dysfunctional (including the range of anxiety disorders) to severe and chronic (such as more involved mental illness like schizophrenia and bipolar disorder). Regardless of manifestation and pronounced symptoms, almost all mental health issues are correlated with and magnified—if not caused by—associated anxiety.

Treating anxiety is necessary to cut off the head of the snake.

Religious leaders

Those who are led by strong spiritual or religious persuasions often feel more comfortable seeking help and advice from trusted leaders in their place of worship or affiliation. The idea is that leaders who share and teach a like-minded orientation of scriptural foundations for living will understand and provide counsel based on God's word and principles.

I am very partial to such an orientation, given my own strong convictions and my belief in the empirical evidence that guidance based upon holy foundations is often comforting and wise. Pastoral counselors must, however, know the breadth and limits of their own training and must respect careful boundaries, and disclose these parameters to those seeking guidance from them.

Spiritual and religious guidance can be combined with professional treatment. There is no inherent conflict, albeit the necessary distinctions between "health" care and "spiritual" care be specified and blended, but not confounded.

There is an old saying: "God heals, but the doctor sends the bill." Religious leaders don't send bills. Wise professionals humbly seek to include God in their efforts to help sufferers.

One of my favorite stories recounts a family in which a troubled adolescent is rebellious. This Christian family is not inclined toward therapy, but instead prays incessantly for their teenager, trusting that only God will heal him of his issues. As they wait for God's intervention, the mother awakens one morning to discover a lump on her breast. Alarmed, she prays until 9:00 a.m., whereupon she calls for a doctor's appointment as soon as possible.

Medication

As already stated, the professional mainstream prioritizes psychotropic medication as the frontline treatment for anxiety and other mental conditions. The underlying assumption is that by manipulating the neurotransmitter irregularities, the problem will be handily addressed (or at least the symptoms will abate.) The biochemical solution is an attempt to provide a quick fix.

Despite the massive evidence that this approach is inadequate and often dangerous, chemical treatment is the accepted norm. A brief review is in order to describe these drugs and what they purport to do, or actually do.

Anxiolytics

Anxiolytics are drugs that quickly calm the central nervous system. They are short-acting and quickly metabolized. These drugs are *de rigueur* prior to surgery to assist in calming patients undergoing understandably stressful procedures. They are also routinely prescribed for the treatment of acute and chronic anxiety.

Among the more common are:

- alprazolam (Xanax)
- chlordiazepoxide (Librium)
- clonazepam (Klonopin)
- diazepam (Valium)
- lorazepam (Ativan)
- buspirone (Buspar)

These drugs are sedatives that act dramatically to reduce panic and the fight-or-flight response of the nervous system. However, they tend to induce tolerance effects (higher and higher dosages needed to achieve the desired effect), and they are highly addictive. Most belong to a class of medications known as benzodiazepines. Manufacturers warn, and physicians know, that these drugs are meant for short-term use. However, that does not discourage desperate anxiety sufferers from overusing or abusing them, even resorting to "doctor shopping" to obtain prescriptions.

Withdrawal from these drugs is painful and often leads to recidivism and relapse. Additionally, rapid withdrawal has a risk of seizures.

Antidepressants

Antidepressants are a class of medications used to treat depressive disorders, anxiety disorders, chronic pain, and sometimes addictions. Common side effects of antidepressants include dry mouth, weight gain, dizziness, headaches, sexual dysfunction, and emotional blunting. These drugs work by prolonging the time that neurotransmitters remain in the synapses (spaces between neurons) before reuptake, thereby supplying the brain with more infusion of neurotransmitters that regulate anxiety and depression.

They typically take some time to build up in the regulatory system, usually several weeks to several months. Often dosages are titrated and may need to be increased or adjusted.

Among the more common of antidepressants are:

- citalopram (Celexa)
- sertraline (Zoloft)
- fluoxetine (Prozac Weekly, Prozac)
- buproprion (Wellbutrin)
- trazodone (Desyrel)
- escitalopram (Lexapro)
- paroxetine (Paxil, Paxil CR)
- venlafaxine (Effexor, Effexor XR)
- vilazodone (Viibryd)
- duloxetine (Cymbalta)

Antidepressants are not thought to be addicting. However, discontinued use often results in the recurrence of symptoms and imbalances. It is also a frequent occurrence that patients who respond well to certain antidepressants do not respond well to them when taken again after a period of discontinuation.

People who take antidepressants usually take them for years, even decades. This is the recommendation of physicians. Many patients I've treated report that they take the medications out of habit, are afraid to stop taking them, or that the medications don't seem to have the desired effect.[4]

Mood stabilizers

Mood stabilizers are a mixed bag of medications that decrease abnormal brain activity by "stabilizing" the flow of neurotransmitters in the brain. They act by inducing time-released inhibition affecting neuronal regulation.

These drugs blunt the highs and lows of mania and dysphoria and are useful in modifying impulsivity delusions of grandeur. They have many undesirable side effects, and patients typically deplore their reduction of thinking and creativity.

Among the more common of mood stabilizers are:

- cariprazine (Vraylar)
- lithium (Eskalith, Lithobid)

Anticonvulsants

Anticonvulsant drugs are traditionally used to treat seizures (epilepsy). They are effective at stabilizing very erratic brain electrical activity and spikes in the EEG that can be dangerous. They are also used off-label to treat manic mood swings.

- lamotrigine (Lamictal)
- valproate (Depakote, Epilim)
- carbamazepine (Tegretol)
- gabapentin (Neurontin)

---

4. Duh: if the meds were working sufficiently, these many patients would likely not be in my office seeking other treatment.

Antipsychotics

These heavy-duty drugs inhibit or decrease psychotic thinking, bizarre ideation, paranoia, and hallucinations. They have many pernicious side effects, including weight gain, fatigue, and eventual tardive dyskinesia (a movement disorder characterized by uncontrollable, abnormal, and repetitive movements of the face, torso, and/or other body parts). Once developed, tardive dyskinesia tends to endure.

Among the more common of antipsychotics are:

- olanzapine (Zyprexa)
- risperidone (Risperdal)
- haloperidol (Haldol)
- quetiapine (Seroquel)
- aripriprazole (Abilify)
- chlorpromazine (Thorazine)

In addition to calming mania (i.e., rampant anxiety and feelings of invincibility), they are known for inducing heavy fatigue. Antipsychotics may serve as "rescue" drugs to contain offensive or aggressive behavior, as well as the distressing subjective symptoms experienced by those who feel or demonstrate that they are losing control. As with other psychotropic medications, they have deleterious effects on organ functions and metabolism, often leading to enormous weight gain, diabetes, and/or other metabolic disorders.

Off-Label Prescribing and Bracket Creep

Physicians are increasingly prescribing medications for purposes other than what the drugs were originally approved for by the FDA. This has been the case for several decades with psychotropic and other drugs, i.e., prescribing newer diabetes medications for weight loss.

For mental health, off-label use is common. Antidepressants are prescribed for anxiety and pain; anticonvulsants (used to treat epilepsy) are prescribed for mania, nerve pain, and used to treat the behavioral disinhibition often seen in conjunction with ADD/ADHD; anxiolytics are used for sleep; antipsychotics are added to treat depression and behaviors, etc.

In his landmark book, *Listening to Prozac* (1993), Dr. Peter Kramer expressed concern about what he called "diagnostic bracket creep," the widening of diagnostic categories to facilitate easier prescribing. He coined the term "cosmetic psychopharmacology" to describe the phenomenon of patients starting to feel "better than well."

The term "bracket creep" sounds almost like a mold or bacteria, but here it refers to the cross migration among symptoms and diagnoses of mental conditions: the "creeping" of one category of mental disorder across the boundaries of others; that is, across once-rigid brackets of diagnostic classification and prescribing conventions.

Regardless of the serious practical concerns and long-term effects of such polypharmacy management, the implication of these practices are striking. Bracket creep evidence shatters older rigid notions about the sanctity, boundaries, and even classification legitimacy of diagnoses held as narrow and indisputable.

The bracket creep encroachment of off-label prescribing (and more fluid diagnostic boundaries) is consistent with robust and pragmatic models of brain functioning. The brain simply does not follow the rigid rules that lend convenience and closure to psychiatric classifications.

When the brain becomes organized and self-regulated, symptoms from seemingly disparate conditions ameliorate. The anxious person sleeps better, the ADD child sheds depression, the migraine patient loses her PMS, the moody person becomes more flexibly focused and less obsessive.

These findings reveal insights about how the brain works and provide pathways for interventions and modifications to treat anxiety and its extended mental health relatives. These theoretical foundations and healing strategies are discussed later in this book.

First, let's take an overview of common contemporary therapeutic practices (besides medication) to treat them.

About Psychotherapy

Before describing different therapies and their roles and utility in treating anxiety, I offer an overview that counterbalances my criticism of the effectiveness of most psychotherapy in treating anxiety. My critical analysis of psychotherapy is not intended to negate the positive experiences and benefits that some have received from such encounters. I don't want to "throw the baby out with the bath water" or dismiss psychotherapy entirely—just as I also acknowledge the limited and careful use of psychotropic medications. Rather, I strive to delineate and distinguish the differences among the appropriate and effective uses of talk therapy and other modalities that are better suited for the treatment of anxiety and many other "mental" and neurologically based problems. The following are some issues and targets that are most amenable to skilled psychotherapeutic intervention.

Reality testing

When the term "reality" is invoked in the context of mental health, it suggests a blanket contrast between *normal* or *conventional* behavior and *psychosis* or *delusions*. In extremes, a person may be partially living in their own mental world that significantly deviates from the real world they inhabit. In such situations, crises and misbehaviors abound, and relationships collide with broken rules.

However, we all live in our own worlds, so to speak: inner worlds composed of values, needs, expectations, and perceptions based on our experiences. Many of these are subtle and not entirely conscious. An individual's "take" on the meaning of someone else's behavior may be errant or misconstrued regarding the intent, motivation, or interpretation of another's feelings or actions.

The concept and modality of *reality testing* in psychology refers to the cognitive process of determining whether one's own perception of events and motivations conforms to (is congruent with) the views of those around them. As a stark example, if there is a sudden rumbling, we in California are quickly prone to suspect an earthquake. Thus the immediate natural reaction may be to ask someone, "Did you feel that?" Or we might turn on the news or go online for verification.

Human interactions and perceptions are saturated and fraught with innumerable ambiguous meanings that can easily be misinterpreted and influenced by personal needs, emotions, and conditioning. The permutations of misinterpretations, misattributions, and hurt feelings are legion. *Did he mean to hurt me? How can she say/think that?*

All women/men/bosses/white people . . . are like that! And so forth. Such *attribution bias*—using current experience to confirm existing biases and beliefs—can readily impede all manner of functioning, relationships, and contentment.

A skilled and sensitive therapist can, through different examples in a patient's reports, open the "recognition aperture" to help the patient evaluate and consider alternative explanations that may be more realistic or adaptive. One technique I use in response to a patient's dogmatic frustration when venting or seeking validation is to evoke an alternative response asking, "Is it *possible* (not likely, but just possible) that there is another explanation for what happened?" I might suggest, "Just use your imagination to predict what so-and-so would say about this. Would her point of view be different from yours? How might we explain that? How would others evaluate this situation?"

Reality testing can be a gentle and expanding method of encouraging patients to become more objective and flexible about situations in which they are rigidly or emotionally mired. It's a tool that takes tutelage and practice to develop more adaptive responses.

Parenting

Not only don't children come with instructions, but few parents are prepared for the substantial and evolving challenges of child rearing. Therapists can play invaluable roles in teaching parents and helping them evaluate and modify their children's and their own behaviors, as well as helping to establish limits, rules, expectations, and consequences. The psychotherapy venue can serve as a forum for establishing family rules and follow-through, as well as for counseling parents through the ambivalent (and long-term) process of deriving satisfaction from parenting, developing healthy parent-child relationships, and learning how to "let go" as their children grow.

Academic and career guidance

Psychologists who are trained in the administration and interpretation of tests can provide valuable services to patients who can benefit from understanding their strengths, weaknesses, talents, and limitations. Using formal assessment, this guidance leans toward outlining useful (and legal) accommodations, advice and predictions about course selection, job applications, and the challenges and likelihood of attaining goals.

Behavioral change—adaptive and maladaptive habits

In addition to my background in developmental psychology, I've had extensive training in learning theory and behavior modification. I use these tools and scientific principles to assist people in changing habits—relinquishing unwanted ones and forming newer adaptive behaviors.

This behavior modification involves using practical learning theory (schedules of reinforcement) to modify actions and habits, as contrasted with cognitive behavior modification, which focuses on reframing, perspective, and thought substitution.

Rather than use thought processes to reframe negative emotions, actual behavior modification teaches people skills of self-observation, self-monitoring, behavioral adjustments, and formative evaluation to methodically shape adaptive (desired) behaviors and extinguish (eliminate) maladaptive (unwanted) behaviors.

Expectations attributions of others' behaviors

Much frustration, disappointment, and conflict arises from unmet or unrealistic expectations and appraisals of the behaviors, feelings, and motivations of others. Commonly and without conscious awareness, most of us project assumptions on others about their intent and motivations. Such projections and attributions can be far from the actual intentions or motivations of those to whom we assign them.

The psychotherapeutic relationship can be a useful forum for developing more objectivity in understanding the actions and feelings of others and developing skills of interacting to cultivate more accuracy and sensitivity.

Observation, evaluation, self-monitoring

An astute therapist can help patients hone and practice important skills to monitor their own behaviors, make careful adjustments, and track and evaluate the effectiveness and results from these strategic tactics. These component skills targeted behavior modification help to change unwanted habits.

Relationship counseling negotiation compromise

The ability to compromise and negotiate win-win situations is crucial to workable relationships. Psychotherapy is a safe venue to develop more flexibility and practice in understanding the positions and needs of others in order to arrive at good deals that work for each party.

In relationships that become stuck, each partner tends to become dug in and feel threatened and defensive about yielding to the wants and needs of the other. A skilled therapist can help break up and work through such logjams and help people come to terms with what conflicts may be resolved and what conflicts may not be.

Over the years, my work with patients has benefited from a model of differentiating and treating separately the elements of *traumas and grievances* in relationships.

Conflict resolution

Conflicts are an inevitable part of human interactions and relationships. Intimate relationships, the lifeblood of emotional fulfillment, can also breed ambivalence, conflict, resentment, and trauma. Any emotional and contractual environment that signals dependence and need also carries the potential for and probability of mixed allegiances: having to meld the ongoing commitment and devotion to the other person in the relationship with the unfettered assertion of one's own identity, values, boundaries, desires, and beliefs.

Such is the potential quandary of becoming dependent and enmeshed with those we need—who sometimes may ignore, deny, disrespect, or infringe upon us. Intimacy can be a double-edged sword with obvious benefits and prospective risks.

Psychotherapy can assist in sorting out the conflicts, frustrations, and unfulfilled expectations conceivably rupturing a relationship. The therapist can guide one or more parties in wending ways through feelings of ambivalence, ambiguity, uncertainty, and resentment. The breaches of trust that can occur are best understood if they are viewed in terms of their origins: *traumas* and *grievances*.

My psychotherapy

I am an acolyte of mentorship. I believe in the value of role model-ing and the guidance that can be so helpful (sometimes life-changing) when a knowledgeable and trusted mentor takes a protégé (or patient) "under his wing." I am fortunate to have experienced such relation-ships, both professionally and personally.

In my college years, I came under the influence and guidance of a skilled therapist. Dr. John changed my life for the better. When I started therapy with him, I was a troubled, traumatized, confused, and desperate young man. Though I was achieving academically, I was lost. At that point, I was recovering from years of trauma, rebellion, and drug use. I had endured much ineffective therapy and aversive medica-tions in my trajectory though crises and rebound from bad decisions.

Dr. John was real and practical. His basic approach toward me be-gan and stayed with a platform that still guides the way I think, and how I approach many of my patients. He said to me, "Mark, do you want to be a winner?"

For me, that was like offering a hungry dog some meat, as I am very competitive, ambitious, and was (at the time) frustrated and needy.

"Sure, I want to be a winner!" I replied.

Dr. John methodically and credibly laid out for me in clear terms what being a winner required and how that applied to my actions: i.e., "Winners do *this*. Losers do that." The implications and directives were unambiguous.

It worked. Learning from him, I gradually reformed my behav-iors and lifestyle to adopt and strengthen more "winner" behaviors and dismiss my "loser" behaviors. Under Dr. John's guidance, my achievement accelerated, my relationships and health improved, and my confidence surged. The combination of my desire and persever-ance, his clarity and leadership, and his approval and reinforcement, gradually and dramatically turned my life around. For that, I am im-measurably grateful.

I am a fortunate example of how effective psychotherapy can be transforming. But the corollary here is that effective psychotherapy must be appropriate and targeted toward the symptoms and conditions for which it is suitable. And it must utilize methods that truly work to attain its goals.

I don't deny that anxiety and depression were part of my troubled history and condition when I worked with Dr. John. But they were not the major or overriding issues. They contributed to and were magnified by the mess I was in. I needed to straighten out my life, values, and habits. The personal relationship with Dr. John was instrumental. I had to get out of anxiety and depression in other ways.

We don't expect dental floss to fill a cavity; or vitamins to eliminate an addiction; or antibiotics to repair a torn ligament. These tools are useful, but not suited for certain jobs. Such is the case with the application of therapies to the effective treatment of anxiety and other persisting negative emotions.

Therapies

Mental health therapies assume a wide range of modalities with scores (if not hundreds) of variations, subtypes, and blends. When asked about their theoretical orientations, many therapists often prefer not to be pinned down or stereotyped, and will often describe themselves as "eclectic," blending the most useful aspects of different approaches.

Nonetheless, recognizing the categories that describe the assumptions and practices of psychotherapies can be useful in understanding the different approaches used among *psychodynamic* therapies, *behavioral* therapies, and *somatic* therapies.

Psychodynamic therapies

Psychodynamic approaches assume that problematic feelings, behaviors, and relationships result from "underlying" psychological conflicts arising from childhood experiences (particularly with parents or parent figures) that have gone unresolved. The "underlying" aspect implies that the patient is not consciously aware of these dynamics and/or how they affect their behavior. Therefore, the role of the therapist is to assist bringing these conflicts, memories, and feelings to the fore and to help the patient "work through" them via therapist guidance and the benefit of present reality and logic. This method assumes that repetitive dysfunctional behaviors can best be changed through the guided professional reemergence of their source, along with the insights and revelations that allow the patient to release previously held (and unaware) patterns of thinking and feeling.

I was trained in traditional psychoanalytic therapy and underwent such treatment myself. I found it to be largely a waste of time and money, based on some antiquated and unverifiable theories. Though some may derive benefit from this extensive and expensive process, I believe this type of psychotherapy is slow, mysterious, and of dubious value in ridding patients of recurrent anxiety.

Behavioral therapies

Behavioral therapies have markedly different assumptions and interventions. Relying on the theory that all behaviors serve some purpose, the therapist analyzes with the patient the cause-and-effect behavior chains that strengthen and maintain (reinforce) behaviors without much regard to the origination or emotional fuel that makes the behaviors continue. The emphasis is upon identifying and altering the "payoff" that maintains the (usually unwanted) behavior—that is, what does the person "get" from habitual responses. By understanding how the stimulus-response connections (reinforcers), once associated with each other, preserve and habituate actions and feelings, patients can modify the linkages and schedules among behaviors to form more adaptive ones. Thus, treatment focuses on observable and measurable antecedents and consequences of current behaviors, rather than what happened in the murky past.

Targeted behavior modification is a useful adjunct to forming adaptive behaviors and quitting maladaptive ones. It is more appropriate for actions than for feelings.

Somatic therapies

Somatic therapies presume a physiological basis for mental health dysfunction, and attempt to treat and relieve problems by addressing the causative physiological malady. Somatic therapies subsume interventions that provide "body inputs" as the gateway to influence and change feelings and aberrant behaviors. (Of course, the medical hardline biological view is indeed a somatic approach that uses pharmaceuticals as the agents of change. The psychopharmaceutical approach deals chemically with the symptoms and bypasses therapist techniques.)

Therapies such as EEG biofeedback (neurofeedback) EMDR (eye movement desensitization and reprocessing), TFT (thought field therapy) are among the better-known treatments that assume and apply physiology for healing. Although not considered mental health therapies, some patients (and doctors) advocate acupuncture and chiropractic as effective interventions for a variety of mental problems, including stress and anxiety.

A myriad less conventional "energy" therapies also purport to target and release harmful patterns stuck in the muscles and nervous system. These techniques are administered through physical touch, including massage, trigger points, Reiki, chakra release, meridian channels, and many others.

Counseling and psychotherapy: individual and group

Most therapies, so-called "talk therapies," assume the traditional format of a licensed therapist talking to a patient on a regular basis (weekly, monthly, etc.) The role of the therapist is to provide validation for the patient's difficult feelings and experiences, a sympathetic ear, and support in the forms of advice, coping strategies, and crisis management.

Since people like to be heard and supported, patients often feel good about seeing their therapists, and they may exit the sessions feeling relaxed and connected. Unfortunately, talk therapy does little (if anything) to relieve anxiety and other emotional anguish on any lasting basis. And how can it? If one accepts the reality that emotional dysfunction is organically/physiologically based, then how can talking about such feelings make them go away? You wouldn't treat cancer or a thyroid condition by talking about it! You must treat the actual pathology. Validating feelings is a first step toward trust and connection, but it doesn't make the problem go away.

Cognitive therapies

A majority of psychotherapies ("talk therapy") use cognitive behavioral strategies to relieve anxiety and other mental health problems. Offered by names like cognitive behavior therapy (CBT) or Dialectical Behavior Therapy (DBT), these interventions occur via the therapist teaching the patient to "reframe" thoughts that accompany distressing feelings. These techniques use logic to evaluate the problematic associations between anxious feelings and the dysfunctional and catastrophizing thoughts that accompany them. The therapist teaches the patient to evaluate the "faulty" connection and substitute more realistic and consonant thoughts, thereby attempting to break the connection and subsume the feelings.

In my experience, such cognitive strategies don't work well at all. No surprise. This is because emotions arise in the brain and nervous system through different pathways than thoughts and cognitive analysis. Negative emotions arise in the *viscera* (the internal organs, particularly in the gut) and are then funneled through organelles in the brain (especially the amygdala) that signal the central nervous system to be on heightened alert (fight-or-flight) because the body senses danger (whether or not the threat is actual, perceived, or potential). Whereupon, the mind creates a narrative to interpret, explain, or justify the alarming feelings and sensations. The feelings and thoughts become entwined in a feedback loop that allows them to associate and perpetuate each other. However, you cannot break this cycle by intervening on the cognitive level. Trying to eradicate negative emotions by imposing logical override is simply *backward*: like putting on shoes first and then socks! One must eliminate the cause of the maladaptive feelings at the source—physiologically, rather than by substitutionary reasoning.

Exposure therapies

Exposure therapies attempt to break associations of fear (phobias) by methodically introducing the fearful patient to the avoided stimulus gradually while the patient is in an induced "relaxed" state. Typically, this happens by the therapist relaxing the patient with some technique to temporarily calm the nerves and then accompanying the patient—first in the office and eventually in the environment where the feared stimulus occurs. The idea is that if the patient can approach the feared stimulus while in a relaxed state, the fear association will diminish and extinguish.

This treatment, known as systematic desensitization, is ineffective. Moreover, it is arduous, painful for the patient and, in my opinion, quite primitive. Full disclosure: many decades ago, I used this method (ineffectively) when it was thought to be the only viable way to eliminate fear and phobias. Given the very effective treatments now available for such conditions, systematic desensitization is as inappropriate as leeches for bloodletting.

Somatic "Power" therapies

Therapies that work by engaging the patient (and symptoms) at a physiological level are *somatic*, in that they cause adaptive changes in the body that translate directly to the reduction and/or elimination of negative emotional states. I sometimes refer to these as "power" therapies, because they are powerful in effect, usually rapid in results, and often transformative in that the outcomes are dramatic beyond a step-wise progression.

EMDR (eye movement desensitization and reprocessing) is a therapy by which the practitioner guides the patient through a series of rapid eye movements while the patient locates painful thoughts and memories. This technique somehow influences the brain to "reprocess" the originating trauma, often resulting in the reduction or resolution of long-held bothersome symptoms.

EMDR is a reputable, widely used and effective technique. I trained in EMDR with its founder, Francine Shapiro, in the early 1990s. I used it with moderate success, but abandoned it in favor of the other methods (discussed below) that I found to be far more successful.

Hypnosis is a venerable psychological method that has been used for many decades. This method uses a variety of *induction* techniques to induce the patient into a deeply relaxed state, during which the therapist tries to implant suggestions to the patient's subconscious that carry over into conscious states, affecting preferences and behaviors. Hypnosis is thought to affect patients at a level of consciousness in which they are "suggestible." Some patients are highly suggestible, whereas others are impervious to this method. Hypnosis has been effective in curbing or eliminating some habits, like smoking.

Since hypnosis involves the power of suggestion in a vulnerable state, many patients (especially those with strong religious convictions) are leery of psychological influences that may expose susceptible patients to potentially unhealthy or even demonic forces.

Hypnosis is a valid and probably underutilized treatment. I have used it successfully in the past. Presently, I prefer to use a neurofeedback technique called *alphatheta* that induces low-frequency physiological and psychological states indirectly through neural feedback without verbal or other suggestive inputs. Alphatheta is an advanced version of neurofeedback that is highly effective for trauma, depression, sleep, and addictions.

Neurofeedback (EEG biofeedback) is a main intervention I have used for many decades. The procedure directly trains brainwaves through the use of computers and specific, carefully calibrated software. The program is based on electrical brain activity that is measured by the electroencephalogram, or EEG.

Neurofeedback permits the brain to function more efficiently and proficiently by taking advantage of the brain's *plasticity*, or ability to adapt and utilize different aspects of itself, promoting this flexibility as advantageous. During neurofeedback training, the patient (and the practitioner) observe the brain in action from moment to moment. The information is displayed a computer screen and simultaneously rewards the brain for changing its activity to more appropriate patterns. This is a gradual transitioning process that affects and conditions any measurable aspect of brain function.

Neurofeedback is training in self-regulation. This self-regulation is a necessary part of good brain function. Self-regulation training makes the brain and central nervous system function more capably. Key to reducing anxiety and other negative emotions, it is among the most effective and enduring methods for treating anxiety. This method is discussed in more detail later.

Thought Field Therapy (TFT) is a method of rapidly and completely eliminating negative emotions. More specifically, it involves a finger-tapping technique that patients perform on themselves to eliminate the negative emotion. (Actually, what gets eliminated is the coded information or "perturbation" that links a negative emotion to a thought, once the thought is attuned. Hence, the name, Thought Field Therapy.) This technique can be learned and self-administered. However, many people find it advisable to seek the help of a trained therapist, particularly for recalcitrant problems that require a more precise and higher level of professional intervention (such as Voice Technology).

Quite frequently, the administration of a single application of this technique can often eradicate a problem that has persisted for years. This has been repeatedly demonstrated, and I have successfully used this powerful procedure in my practice thousands of times. Thought Field Therapy (TFT) is discussed later in more detail.

Summary of Mental Health Treatments

Those who suffer chronically with anxiety and other negative emotions are beset with painful and handicapping conditions that impede and impair their health, functioning, and quality of life. The available mainstream recourses typically confront sufferers and patients with a revolving door of limited options, often headlined by harsh and side-effect-laden drugs that offer temporary and partial relief without solving the underlying problems.

Many therapies, traditional and otherwise, purport to treat the malaise, but offer little, if any, help and rely upon faulty theories and methods to alleviate mental health distress.

For the dysfunction that plagues millions of suffers, I've found that EEG neurofeedback and Thought Field Therapy deliver the best, safest, and most enduring effects for freeing people from debilitating anxiety, other negative emotions, and the maladaptive behaviors that often accompany these handicaps.

Succeeding chapters explain these effective treatments in greater detail and provide a pathway to break free from anxiety, fears, worry, and obsessive negative thinking.

CHAPTER 5

Addiction and the Anxiety Withdrawal Cycle

The Nature of Addiction

For a significant percentage of our population, addiction is front and center in its stranglehold upon health and productive functioning. Whether an addiction involves a substance or a behavior that is destructive, many in its throes are somewhere in the cycle of thinking about indulging, indulging, or recovering from indulgence.

Addictions are complex syndromes that afflict health, develop maladaptive behaviors and dependencies, and typically impair functioning in relationships, productivity, and self-care for millions. Addictions weaken self-confidence and self-esteem, bring conflicts and negative emotions, and erode our sense of responsibility for the resulting dysfunction that follows. Central to any addiction are problems with self-management, self-control, obsessive thinking, and neurological dysregulation.

Addiction goes hand-in-hand with anxiety. The brain and nervous system in states of disrepair and deprivation due to addiction will be anxious, both biologically and psychologically. Since most people live under conditions of great stress and duress (internal and environmental), and the development of adequate coping resources and self-regulation mechanisms is challenging, many of us rely upon substances or behaviors that blunt the pain and negative emotions and provide temporary escape. This inevitably develops maladaptive habits that reinforce the problem and further erodes coping skills.

Pandemic or Prototype?

Addictions of various types are pervasive. Though we think of them as illnesses (as they often are) and deviations from biological normalcy (which they definitely are), those with some type of addiction are so common that, statistically, addictions fall within the norm.[5]

Addictions vary from food to behaviors to drugs. This is of great concern, especially in light of the increase in lethal illicit drug supplies and overdoses. Addiction, tobacco smoking and chewing, and alcoholism are nothing new. Current trends and supporting research highlight an emerging awareness of food addiction, as more people develop health problems directly related to their diet. Biological, economic, and sociological influences collude to encourage us eat too much and eat foods that eventually make us sick.

The food processing industry has come under scrutiny for advanced manufacturing and marketing that manipulate to their advantage our inherent attraction (and resulting addiction) to fats, sweets, and salt. The wide availability of unnatural and cheap foods pander to immediate gratification and take advantage of genetic programming that predisposes us to unwitting caloric storage. A multitude of social, political, and economical influences keep millions of people marginal and unable to provide adequately for themselves and families, which create a sure recipe for many kinds of addictions. Addictions are pandemic, including and adhering to determinants that are biological, social, destructive, and essentially contagious, i.e. via peers and life pressures rather than microbes.[6]

---

5. Normal in the statistical sense refers to occurrences within 95 percent of the population on the observed variable or characteristic. Average, statistically, falls within the middle 50 percent of the population.
6. While obviously involving microbes, diseases such as AIDS and hepatitis are among those spread by addictions.

The propensity to become addicted is practically wired into our need to escape pain, reduce stress, and quell anxiety. This does not mean that addiction is inevitable, but addiction is a likely cohort of anxiety that is facilitated by poor resilience, vulnerable lifestyles, and lack of adequate resources and interventions to protect ourselves, weather adversity and conflict, and develop adequate sustainable self-regulation, self-soothing mechanisms, and overall self-control.

The Addiction-Anxiety Connection

Addiction is a dependency on some substance or activity that causes some degree of harm to, or interference with, a person's life. The dependency is powered by the tranquilizing (i.e., anxiety masking) effect of the substance or activity.

Addictions originate from anxiety, and all addictions are responses to relieving (or masking) anxiety. The seminal role of anxiety in forming and sustaining addictions doesn't negate or omit the biology of physiological dependence on certain substances, or the build-up of tolerance. Clearly, the brain becomes accustomed to some chemicals (such as opiates or alcohol) in a manner that creates physiological withdrawal and the possibility of severe illness or death if withdrawal is too acute or sudden. The pernicious and stubborn recurrence of anxiety develops a cycle of addiction and withdrawal in the first place that can soon lead to physiological dependence in addition to more pervasive anxiety.

Addiction generates the belief that the addicted person cannot live without the necessary substance/object/behavior. In these cases, the challenge to conquering addictions involves instituting a safe and viable way of *eliminating anxiety*. Once this is in place, habits can be changed, along with revising the belief that one *must* engage or indulge in the desires that propel the addictive substance or behavior.

Anxiety is a painful emotion to experience and is worsened when it has no apparent cause and resurfaces repeatedly without "logical" provocation. Anxious people feel bad due to the anxiety, and also feel sheepish when the emotion makes no sense.

If an anxious person can "take" something or do something that blocks awareness of the anxiety, they feel tremendous relief. The relieved person feels calm, serene, tranquilized, and temporarily free of the agonizing feeling of anxiety. The relief feels so good that it makes a profound impression on their body and mind. Though many addicts are aware of this sequence of actions leading to addiction, not every addict is aware of the process while it is occurring. This sequence happens to each addict at a profound level of being, regardless of the conscious awareness.

The process of addiction creates a state of self-sabotage in the addict. This state makes it especially difficult to overcome the addiction because it drives the addict to engage in self-defeating activities and to become his own worst enemy, such as not doing a simple treatment that can eliminate the addictive urge.

We don't fully know why certain substances or activities mask anxiety. Some drugs appear to physically block awareness of anxiety, via nervous system or brain neurotransmitters, and certain activities such as thumb-sucking or hair-pulling appear to be intrinsically soothing to some individuals, with the apparent comfort of the activity blocking awareness of anxiety.

The term "addiction" is often used rather loosely, which sometimes leads to misunderstanding. For example, some might postulate addiction to sports or books. But this questionable terminology is meant to indicate a strong or intense fondness for sports or books. However, in a psychological or medical sense, the term "addicted" has the clear implication of indicating a problem—and problem that interferes with a person's life, functioning, health, or well-being to some degree. To call natural, wholesome, and healthy good feelings an addiction is not reasonable. To feel good physically and mentally naturally, without drugs, is a sign and a consequence of good general health.

Habit and Addiction

Many people confuse habits and addictions despite the significant difference between the two. A *habit* is a behavior pattern that is so established in our behavioral repertoire that it is usually carried out regularly without conscious effort. Since a certain amount of effort goes into establishing a habit, a certain effort is typically required to change a habit.

A good example of a habit is how we train ourselves to automatically remove the car keys when we leave our car. When we go to a car wash, a car repair, or leave our car with a valet parking service, a special conscious effort is required in order to not walk off with the car keys when we shouldn't.

When we make the conscious effort, many habits are not that difficult to change; the essence is remembering to be conscious about it. People sometimes mistake habits for addictions. They can be coupled, but have fundamental differences. In addiction, no matter how conscious one is, the addictive urge is rather compelling or overwhelming, depending upon the severity of the addiction.

Addictions, unlike most habits, are extremely difficult to give up. In the case of an addiction, a person is driven and compulsive; but in the case of habits, the person's actions represent highly learned activities that are often amenable to conscious efforts to change.

Anxiety and Addiction

Legions of people in the world, even though not in chronic physical pain or in combat, feel just as bad or worse as those who are in chronic physical pain. These people suffer from anxiety.

Anxiety is the presence of fear or nervous system overarousal when there is no objective external reason to be afraid or to maintain the overarousal. While others may dismiss or even scoff at *perseverative*[7] anxiety, its sufferers know how inappropriate their anxiety is. This knowledge only complicates their plight, for they suffer not only from overbearing anxiety, but also from the embarrassment and self-deprecation that accrues from having the problem.

Addiction problems result from the anxiety-masking effects of abusing substances or engaging in counterproductive or self-defeating activities. The essence of all addiction is a powerful, often overwhelming,

---

7. Perseverative, in psychology is term used to indicate continued responding on a perceptual, emotional, cognitive, or behavioral level in the absence of the original or appropriate stimulus; think of the afterimage when you look at the sun or a bright light and then look away.

urge to consume an anxiety-reducing substance or participate in an anxiety-reducing activity. An addiction is a behavior pattern characterized by a strong urge to act in a way that compromises the independence of will and its influence over the determinants of behavior. Addictions are "have-to-do" behaviors that persist despite the known harm they bring.

Addictions include using drugs and chemicals that alter consciousness and state of arousal and typically involve the ingestion of tranquilizers, pain pills, alcohol, tobacco, cocaine, meth, heroin, and excess food. They also include a range of behavioral addictions, which are epitomized by the excesses found in obsessive-compulsive disorders. People can even become addicted to behaviors that are natural and/or instinctual, such as sex or anger. In its appropriate context, sex is not considered an addiction. However, sex can become an all-consuming behavior that can be carried to excess and be harmful. The excessive conduct reflects an effort to reduce or mask overwhelming anxiety. Despite his legendary sexual "conquests," Casanova, the ultimate iconic *ladies' man*, was incapable of living normally. Rather, he was the victim of his own overpowering sexual addiction.

Though addictive syndromes contain many variations, the common denominator that is operative in all addictions is the *addictive urge*: the desire for the relief that maintains the addiction. The unrelieved or temporarily assuaged urge results in a state of withdrawal, thus perpetuating the dysfunctional cycle.

Foundation of the Addictive Urge

Anxiety is the trigger for all addictive urges, and addressing the addictive urge (or craving) is the basis of effective treatment for any addiction. Addictive substances or behaviors serve the purpose of masking anxiety, but do not eliminate anxiety. *Withdrawal* is the formerly hidden anxiety coming back into the realm of conscious awareness and provoking crises. The anxiety-addiction connection is key to understanding and successfully treating addictions.

Addiction is a dependency on a certain substance or activity that causes some degree of harm to, or interference with, a person's life. The dependency is powered by the tranquilizing (i.e., anxiety-masking) effect of the substance or activity. If an anxious person ingests something or does something that blocks awareness of the anxiety, they feel tremendous relief; the person feels calm, serene, tranquilized, and temporarily free of the agonizing feeling of anxiety. The relief feels so good that it makes a profound impression on the body and the mind of the anxiety victim. Though many addicts are aware of the actual underlying dynamics of the process, this sequence happens to each addict at a profound level of being, irrespective of the level of conscious awareness.

Research is progressively uncovering information about changes in brain function and structure resulting from repeated indulgence. Newer findings in the realm of "hard" drugs like methamphetamine, cocaine, opiates, and also alcohol suggest that usage itself changes the brain's ability and response capacities with regard to satiety and satisfaction. *Reward deficiency syndrome* is a popular hypothesis linking drug usage to the brain's failure to derive pleasure from previously satisfying experiences once it has experienced the intense highs induced by certain substances. However, changes in pleasure thresholds in the brain do not mitigate the originating problem of the addictive urge and its destructive stranglehold over adaptive goal-driven behavior. The imminence of the resurgent addictive urge supersedes values, planning, and internal organization, as it demands palliation of primitive fight-or-flight hyperarousal. We are faced with the problem of how to reduce or eliminate the addictive urge.

Eliminate the Addictive Urge

Yielding to a temptation (impulse and habit) to indulge in one's addictive behavior has multiple influences, but the strongest recurrent component is the addictive urge, rooted in the cycle of withdrawal and anxiety. The relief provided by indulgence is temporary; and when it recedes, the inevitable intrusion of discomfort and anxiety preoccupies and propels the sufferer to use again, as it seems the only memorized means of relief.

We have many ways to counter the anxiety that drives the urge to indulge (i.e., combat the anxiety). Exercise, taking appropriate medication, distraction through some activity or interaction, calling a sponsor or friend, etc., are among the palliative and diversionary tactics the can reduce, defer, or forestall the anxiety that makes people want to use. Having tools and techniques to subdue anxiety and negate the addictive urge that predictably accompanies withdrawal is crucial for addicts to overcome their addictions. Though this is not the only issue in addictions, it is fundamental to the healing and recovery process.

Consider this example: in playing hockey, there are many skills needed to play, along with strategies, techniques, and team collaboration. However, being able to skate well is fundamental to playing the sport. Without facile skating and good physical condition, the other elements will not suffice. Similarly, breaking the anxiety-addiction connection by eliminating the predictable anxiety is necessary to gain a foothold on self-control, brain balance, and habit reformation.

Finding the most effective formula, technique, or practice that provides that fundamental ability to "skate" well enough to break the anxiety-addiction connection is essential. In my decades of treating anxiety and addictions, I've found nothing that surpasses the use of TFT (Thought Field Therapy) for rapid, effective, and expedient elimination of anxiety. In addition to professional intervention (including using Voice Technology by phone), I provide patients with self-help applications of TFT that enables them to treat themselves when anxious withdrawal strikes and which empowers them to subdue their anxiety and regain control and more volition over their actions and choices.

TFT intervention is a powerful and broad-based treatment that applies to all forms of anxiety and other negative emotions, and is explained in detail in Part II Solutions.

Dealing effectively, primarily, early, and often is key to successful treatment of any addiction. Though we typically think of addictions as substance abuse disorders, smoking, overeating, or gambling or sexual compulsions, the brain addictions net spreads widely to subsume obsessive-compulsive behaviors, such as nail-biting, hair-pulling, and body-picking.

The addiction domain also extends to include chronic yelling and extreme anger outbursts. These are bad habits that develop into addictive behavior patterns that release steam from cumulative frustration and anxiety.

A person who thinks that yelling at family or others is "necessary" because they won't listen or will fail to follow directions, should consider that:

1. Yelling reinforces the ignoring or defying on the part of the targets, as well as conditioning them to wait for a raised voice before they respond.

2. The yeller is unwittingly self-training to depend upon yelling to release anxiety (whether or not it gets the desired behavioral result).

Even though alcohol, fentanyl, or other substances may not be the problem, we can be vulnerable and succumb to yelling or angry outbursts as addictive manifestations of quelling our anxiety.

If a person is determined to get a handle on the pernicious anxiety-withdrawal connection, they must address and defeat the sneaky and persistent addictive urge.

CHAPTER 6

Negative Thinking and Obsessive Worrying

Each of us has conversations in our mind. The natural operation of cognition involves thought processes that combine language, sensations and feelings, perceptions, and memories into a running or sporadic narrative that chronicles events, interprets their meaning and significance, and makes hypotheses or predictions about the future.

Whereas the mind's narrative and ruminations are continuous, sometimes they can be interfering or bothersome. Intrusive thoughts can recur along with criticisms and worries that may overtake and flood our minds with negative thoughts, images, and feelings, obsessively repeated, and cynical or gloomy forecasts and expectations.

Negative thoughts, obsessive rumination, and worrying are closely tied with anxiety. The fight-or-flight response that prompts anxiety gives rise to racing thoughts and fearful imaginations. The flood of negative thoughts and incessant worrying, in turn, promotes and justifies the physiological anxiety response of the nervous system. They feed and reinforce each other. Repetition of this pattern tends to build self-effacing brain habits, whereby the "thinker" eventually feels out of control and victimized by negative thinking that won't subside. Even though the person recognizes this pattern as an endless and meaningless loop, he may feel powerless to quiet and control it. This annoyance is akin to a broken record where, in the music of yesteryear, the phonograph needle is stuck in a record scratch and just keeps playing the same phrase over and over again.

In my experience, negative thoughts, obsessive rumination, and worrying are pervasive, inflicting inhibition, anxiety, and misery on a vast swath of the population. These symptoms are among the chief complaints of patients in my clinical practice. Though we all have occasional or periodic bouts of worry, self-criticism, and adverse anticipation, some people are persistently beset by negativity and self-absorption. This is a painful way to live.

Others are naturally and habitually inclined to look at the dark or problematic side of things with a habit of "looking at the hole instead of the donut." Some of this disposition has genetic roots. About one sixth of the population develops with a cautious disposition, given to suspecting the downside, and even becoming perfectionistic. However, there are positive features of this temperament. Caution and detail orientation can complement and balance the tendencies of others to be impulsive and plunge headlong into decisions and actions without prudent evaluation of risks. But excessive caution, fear, and/or anticipating and compensating for every potential mishap or error often results in delays, procrastination, abject avoidance, frustration, and inefficiency.

Traumatic and disappointing life experiences relegate many people to become mistrustful and pessimistic. Thus they tend to view and interpret events in the least favorable light. They have fractured relationships and difficulty living with themselves and others. Sometimes these patterns coalesce into personality disorders. In extreme cases, such people have trouble changing and don't even want to get better, clinging to the belief that their views on accuracy and corrupt human nature are the most realistic way to approach life. They often justify their attitude with examples of being right about how many things have turned out badly.

Interestingly, in my graduate school research (decades ago), I conducted experiments (subsequently published) in which troubled high school students were tasked with keeping records of their attendance and tardies. The results (replicated and confirmed by later research) showed that the subjects were significantly more accurate in tracking negative behaviors than positive ones. These findings are consistent with a plethora of research suggesting that we are more accurately attentive to our flaws than to our successes. This has implications for self-awareness, self-confidence (both too much and too little), and the need to monitor our behaviors with some objective standards to balance our subjective perceptions.

For the purpose of addressing negative, pessimistic, or obsessive thinking, we must provide insight and resources for restoring people's control over their minds and anxieties, while understanding that a percentage of the population will naturally be geared toward focusing on the downside. Those who seek help and relief from the torment of living inside their own head are more interested in eliminating negative thoughts and intrusions than justifying their negative orientation.

Review and Recognition

We observe and recognize in ourselves the chatter in our minds that is constant, sometimes in the background, and at other times loud, insistent, relentless, and controlling. It's tempting to "talk back" to this chatter (narrative, voice-over), telling it to be quiet, countering its "opinion," or begging it to recede. Undoubtedly, you may have noticed that fighting it has little helpful effect.

Many people feel controlled or consumed by obsessive inner thoughts and worries, which can cumulatively produce feelings of losing control of one's mind. Such tendencies are often centered around or accompanied by fears, phobias, or recurrent triggers of anxiety.

Before examining what can be done to quiet the thoughts and reduce anxiety, see if you recognize the following patterns:

Are You A Worrier?

Many people resign themselves to a self-described "worrying personality." They may even (painfully) acknowledge and adopt the characterization that others have labeled them, as a "worrywart." Life is full of challenges and provocations for each of us. But many suffer from the constant fear of the unknown, the tendency to forecast "gloom-and-doom" negative predictions, endless "what ifs," and a compelling focus on concerns about health, finances, approval, etc.

If the brain cannot turn off the endless cycle of worry, an unnatural problem occurs. We need the ability to put aside thoughts and control excessive tendencies to dwell on provocative nervous system responses that elicit and magnify negative emotions. Otherwise the mind recreates and reinforces the imagery and habits that bring unpleasant thoughts and negative forecasting to our predominate consciousness and repetitive thinking.

I have long observed that human reasoning tends to "justify" (rationalize) the visceral promptings of the emotional brain. It's part of our nature to "invent" explanations that support emotional states. This allows a sort of congruence between the rational mind and the emotions in order to interpret and explain our experiences and inner stirrings. However, problems arise and continue when the emotional system becomes the source of interpreting reality and then necessarily justifying it. In this odd and elusive internal process, the mind decides that it is "necessary and appropriate" to worry and fret, given all the obvious or latent dangers that surround us or have potential for harm. Thus worrying often becomes an ingrained and justified habit, leaving worriers fretting with a proactive and "just-in-case" mindset.

Obsessive Thinking and Rumination

Whereas worrying is a broad tendency to "anticipate with anxiety" what might happen, obsessive thinking carries anxiety a significant step further. Obsessive thinking is focusing on persistent—usually unwanted—thoughts or thought patterns that have a disturbing quality. The obsession lies in the intrusive nature of the thoughts; they simply take over, recur, and tend to dominate conscious awareness. This intrusion and its concurrent loss of control are understandably highly upsetting and nerve-wracking; the individual can't escape his own brain!

People beset by obsessions often do things or indulge in substances to reduce the intolerable anxiety. Self-medication is common and can lead to addictions and substance abuse. Another "relief" that sufferers resort to is engaging in compulsive behaviors wherein the purpose is only to mollify or temporarily reduce the anxiety. "Checking" things (ovens, lights, doors), ritual counting, or word repetitions, etc., are some compulsive behaviors that serve to temporarily palliate the obsessive mind. They are not solutions though, and such behaviors can frequently escalate into consuming and disturbing compulsions and tics.

Sufferers come to believe that if they don't perform these behaviors or cater to these overruling thoughts, bad things will happen.

Imagining the Worst

Ironically, the anxious person may be erroneously faulted or even self-accused of being his own worst enemy. A couple of wry sayings illustrate this problem.

The first was told to me as a Yiddish proverb: *Vos der mensch ken alts ibertrachten, ken der ergster soyna im nisht vinchen."* (What people can think up for themselves, their own worst enemies couldn't wish upon them.)

The second is attributed to Mark Twain: "I've lived through some terrible things in my life, some of which actually happened."

Indeed, some people can't refrain from worrying and imagining the worst. They create and embellish a fantasy world where they are condemned to threatening circumstances, potential dangers, and almost certain disapproval from others.

Self-Help for Countering Obsessive Thinking

With the realization that fighting off intrusive or obsessive thinking doesn't work well, here is a contextual framework that may help you work around the mind's pestering with more success. Consider these principles to counter and defuse such thinking.

Principle of Observation

It might seem obvious that we *observe* things. Observe can mean *watch, look at, notice* or even *witness* with a keen attention for salient or meaningful indications or details, or further, *recognize* patterns in recurring events or stimuli.

Most people react to intrusive or bothersome thoughts with an emotional response. Though natural, this reaction gets in the way of objective observation. In accord with scientific method, objective observation requires denoting occurrences independent of one's "investment" in outcomes or their frequency of occurrence. You can train yourself to observe your obsessive thoughts and separate them from your emotional or invested response (e.g., "Stop bothering me. Go away!!"). This is helpful because it allows you to watch your mind's busyness and impulsivity. It also works to establish a sense of yourself that is independent of the besieging thoughts, which is a step toward taking control. An additional aspect of observation you might employ is noting how many of your thoughts recur, at what times or environments they seem more intense, and how bothersome the become (e.g., a subjective rating scale, where 10 is the worst, and 1 is "Okay, they're there, but so what?"). Practicing such self-monitoring (*casually*—without adding it to obsessive burdens) builds your skills as an observer, removed somewhat from the reactive impact of the thoughts.

This doesn't necessarily stop troublesome thoughts, but it sets the stage for the helpful tactic of *detachment*.

Principle of Detachment

Making sense of the world and negotiating between the stimuli and demands of external and internal events necessitates a balancing act between becoming involved in thoughts and emotions and keeping them from taking over. The involvement aspect—necessary for motivation, positive feelings, and appropriate action—is called *attachment*. We need to form investments, connections, care, and passion in order to function and to have meaningful relationships. Complementing such involvement, we must be able to distance ourselves from becoming overly absorbed or preoccupied with thoughts, planning, expectations, and concerns about what has or might happen. This is known as *detachment*. Professionals serving clients (e.g., accountants) or patients (health care workers) must detach from personal emotional involvement in order to do their jobs properly. Surgeons typically do not operate on family members.

A working balance between attachment and detachment facilitates drive, motivation, emotional affection, and connection with the ability to calm down, subdue anxiety, and retain perspective. Sometimes people who are aloof or emotionally unavailable are described as detached. That is not the meaning or context here in regard to controlling inner mind functioning.

The principle of detachment is extremely useful in separating oneself from the intrusion and overwhelm of unwanted thoughts. With some practice (and perhaps professional intervention to assist), it becomes quite doable to detach from objectionable thoughts buzzing around inside your head. I refer to this type of detachment as *permeability*.

Many people who practice meditation, a discipline that has been practiced for thousands of years, find this quite helpful. Meditation allows one to detach from thought involvement; but it takes time, lots of practice, and consistency to yield the most satisfying results.

You can practice a quicker and more utilitarian version of detachment by developing the habit of *permeability*. Permeability is the implementation of allowing mental and emotional intrusions to "pass through" your thought narrative, so that you do not have to become attached to them. Essentially, permeability is the ability to exercise detachment, to allow the mantra of "This too shall pass" to comfort and replace any distress resulting from an overinvolvement with something frustrating, painful, oppressive, or that causes suffering. Permeability is a cultivation of observation: you observe your thoughts along with your spontaneous impulses or emotional reactions to them, and then let them go.

Sometimes, I use an image of clouds moving across the sky, or watching your thoughts, desires, temptations, or frustrations roll along on a conveyor belt. Imagine watching the conveyor belt at a baggage claim move along with all sorts of baggage (e.g., your thoughts) that is not yours. You look at the bags, you may be intrigued or tempted, but they are not *yours*. You observe and let them go. If they come around again, you just notice them and let them pass by until you are no longer interested.

Permeability lets your tumultuous or worrisome thoughts pass through filters of overreactions, frustrations, or sensitivities. Permeability is a great antidote to overwhelming thought patterns. Note that permeability does not involve willpower or struggle. Though somewhat conscious and volitional at first, this is not a white-knuckled battle against a strong adversary. Permeability applies the exercise of acceptance of the unwanted mental activity, while dismissing its insistent hold on the mind. You become free to entertain the thoughts or to disregard them. As you allow a more permeable response to your unwanted thoughts, feelings, and speculations, you will find a renewed sense of control and discretion over your mind chatter and provocations to anxiety that it invokes.

Principle of Preclusion and Preemption

Objective observation, detachment, and permeability are useful tools in countering obsessive thinking through passive methods for not reacting to provoking thoughts and feelings. You can also harness strategic and skillful actions to defuse or drive away unwanted insistent thoughts. By using the principle of *preclusion and preemption*, you take charge of your mind by giving it something else to do. To preclude is to prevent or obstruct; to preempt is similar, connoting to block or avert. In essence, you interrupt your mind's habit of cavorting recklessly by introducing some mental activity that is incompatible with worrying, looping, negativity, etc.

Let me share with you the precursors of my learning about this as a child. My father was a humorist, albeit in some cynical and unhealthy ways. He delighted in teasing people. One of his "pranks" was to give me Ritz crackers sandwiched with peanut butter (which I loved). As I chewed the sticky stuff, he'd pull out a dollar bill and say, "Now whistle if you want this." Invariably, this resulted in my spitting the food, whereupon my mother berated my father, and a typical family argument ensued. More drama and trauma . . . but you get the point about incompatibility and distraction.

Just as our physiology does not facilitate digesting, relaxing, or long-term planning while in fight-or-flight mode, our mind cannot host worries when it is occupied by volitional tasks requiring intention and focus. Thus, by intentionally focusing on certain thoughts, topics, feelings, memories, or preferences, you can redirect your mind by putting favored items ahead in the queue. You can learn to "keep the dog mind busy." Dog owners (particularly with certain breeds) know that dogs live in the present, love to play, and need something to do or chew.

If you don't provide your dog with some items or activities that are allowable, the dog will likely find mischief. Similarly, your mind can misbehave like a poorly trained dog. It will "chew" your thoughts and feelings into tearful tatters!

Be advised that the technique of using the principle of *preclusion and preemption* is not thought-stopping or reframing. Rather, by purposefully redirecting your mind from fixation and looping to intentional, focused, positively tinged content, you volitionally host pleasant memories, feelings, and potentials.

Try using this principle of incompatibility to substitute hedonic thoughts and images for fixated repetitious annoyances.

And remember: you can't whistle while chewing crackers and peanut butter.

Practical Tips for Implementation of Preclusion and Preemption

Gratitude

Complaining, stressing, cursing your plight, or feeling sorry for yourself crowd out gratitude. The converse also holds true. Gratitude is an attitude that pushes negative thoughts far away.

When I get on a roll, thinking about all the things I'm grateful for, I'm overcome with humility and the essence of peace. You needn't be "grateful" for negative thoughts, anxiety, or pain; but you can embrace gratefulness for your other wonderful fortunes and for the grace to endure adversity and hardship. Muster some credit to God and yourself: the anguish has not yet killed you.

Joy Buckets

I have my own collection of what I call "joy buckets." Like music playlists from which I can play favorite songs to enjoy, boost mood, and get *in the zone*, I have internal playlists of thoughts that bring me gratification and pleasure. Like different genres of music, my joy bucket playlists consist of slow and relaxing rhythms, soulful pleadings, emotional romantic memory ballads, and upbeat tempos.

Typically, I pluck from a bucket the images and personas of people I know and like, people who regard and treat me favorably, memories of wonderful times, jokes and ironies that make me laugh, things I've done well, things I'm looking forward to, etc. My joy buckets are filled with items from the next categories.

Prayer

I never tire of prayer. It's an appetite that keeps returning. I've learned to depend upon it. Though I am rarely satisfied with my amount or attention to prayer, and it's easy to get distracted or forget, I keep returning to prayer to soothe, quiet, and encourage my mind. Many Bible verses comfort and fulfill me. I read and repeat them ritualistically (not compulsively), and they overcome me with peace, even in the midst of apprehension and travails. This does require practice and belief. Do try it.

The power of God's Word and spirit has a consistent and remarkable effect on reducing anxiety, fear, and worry. Additionally, focusing on God's unerring Word implants positive messages to the conscious and subconscious mind and spirit

Self-reinforcement

As a student and practitioner of behavior modification for decades, I rely on self-reinforcement as a method of implanting positive images and overriding interfering self-talk. Reinforcement is a natural, inadvertent, or intentional process whereby a consequence that follows a particular stimulus or event strengthens the probability that its antecedent will reoccur. An association forms in the mind's perception and memory that connects cause and effect and becomes habit.

Rewards and praise are types of reinforcement typically understood, but any consequence that raises the likelihood of a behavior reoccurring is a reinforcer. Thus, undesirable habits, such as yelling or nail-biting, are also reinforced behaviors.

Self-reinforcement occurs when you provide the consequence that strengthens a response (including thoughts), rather than responding to a consequence given by someone else or the circumstances.. I use self-reinforcement regularly by reminding myself of things I've done well, accomplishments, sacrifices for others, compliments I've received, positive thoughts and energy I've marshaled. This routine "patting myself on the back" is based upon evidence and feedback from others rather than only aggrandizing myself with ego boosts. Gratitude, compassion, and forgiveness play major roles in the ways I reinforce myself.

Humor

Laughing out loud (or silently) is a great way to infuse incompatibility with fretting, anxiety, and negativity. Use the abundant comical parts of life to offset the pain. Here's a joke to launch your funny bone: *It was raining so hard in the city, I saw Superman get into a taxi.*

Noble, excellent, lovely, true . . .

There is a Bible verse I keep returning to as a model for inspiring positive, healthy thinking:

> *Finally, brothers and sisters, whatever is true, whatever is noble, whatever is right, whatever is pure, whatever is lovely, whatever is pure, whatever is lovely, whatever is admirable—if anything is excellent or praiseworthy—think about such things.*
>
> —Philippians 4:8

An image that always stands out for me is that of a mother nurturing and protecting her child. Many other images ring true and consonant with what this verse describes and exhorts:

> *Cast all your anxiety on him because he cares for you.* 1 Peter 5:7

Do for Others

A guiding principle that keeps me in line and gives me purpose is my commitment to serve others. When my mind is racing, negative, cynical, or funky, I conjecture ways I might do something that others need or that would be helpful to them. These plans may be realistic or imaginary, but they always jolt my mind back from self-preoccupation and studying my own belly button.

Perfectionism

In the realm of obsessive thinking, critical negativity, worry, and recrimination, perfectionism ranks prominently in the hierarchy of anxiety and self-torment. Perfectionism is not a single entity, but rather a spectrum that from adaptive conscientiousness (attention to detail, fastidiousness, diligence, thoroughness) to maladaptive views and habits (fussiness, nitpicking, hairsplitting, inability to tolerate error).

Perfectionism describes standards that do not allow for flaws. Beyond the need for high quality and adherence to expectations, perfectionists live in a parsed reality far more stringent than that recognized and inhabited by those more flexible. Perfectionism creates tension, anxiety, and conflict. Perfectionists manifest their need for control by finding fault pervasively. Outcomes and people (especially themselves) are rarely good enough. They always find some other detail to fix, improve upon, or complete. This outlook results in delays, missing deadlines, and much frustration for the perfectionist and for those with whom they interact. Whereas perfectionists may tout accuracy, correctness, or doing things by the book, typically their exaggerated meticulousness goes overboard. It is hard to live with themselves and others.

As an example of the endless frustration of perfectionism, consider Zeno's dichotomy paradox:

Suppose someone wishes to get from point A to point B. First, they must move halfway.

Then they must go half of the remaining way.

Continuing in this manner, there will always be some small distance remaining, and the goal would never actually be reached.

There will always be another number to add in a series such as $1 + 1/2 + 1/4 + 1/8 + 1/16 + \ldots$

So motion from any point A to any different point B seems an impossibility. Going half the distance to a destination means you will never reach it, since you will have to go halfway from wherever you are.

As denoted earlier, about one sixth of the population develops a cautious disposition, given to suspecting the downside and even becoming perfectionistic. Along with the positive features of this temperament, there lurks the vulnerability of becoming excessive with this habit and trait.

The challenge for perfectionists is to learn better tolerance of life's fuzziness, unevenness, entropy, and surprises. They also must develop flexibility, forgiveness, and the habit of letting go and detaching. For perfectionists, the rules and principles of easing anxiety, compromising, and living in the world as it is (rather than as desired) apply in spades. It's a tall order, but the rewards—even for slight progress—are enormous.

Professional Help for Countering Obsessive and Negative Thinking

Among the millions of people who struggle with anxiety, obsessive rumination, and negative thinking, many seek professional help.

As discussed previously, the treatments typically offered by mainstream and conventional sources are limited in scope, mostly ineffective, and can have harmful side effects. Sufferers seeking help are usually led toward medications that—in my view and in the experience of most patients who take them—work temporarily and then stop working; they come with unpleasant side effects, harmful results on the brain and body, addictive properties, and lack lasting benefit or contributions to developing self-control. Psychopharmacology is most often a poor solution for anxiety and intrusive or negative thinking. As explained earlier, cognitive behavioral interventions also lack lasting effectiveness due to fundamental mistaken assumptions about and misalignment with the natural biological order and relationship between thoughts and emotions.

Fortunately, technological treatments exist that work well to reduce and even eliminate anxiety as well as to temper the persistent overwhelm of intrusive and obsessive thinking, compulsions, and negativity. Though these treatments are not new (in fact, they are supported by decades of research and clinical evidence), they are not prominent on the radar or recommendations offered by the mainstream. This is changing, as more people with emotional suffering discover and benefit from these effective, nondrug treatments.

For decades, I have employed a combination of Voice Technology, Thought Field Therapy, and EEG neurofeedback to defeat anxiety. The success rate is astoundingly high, and these treatments are safe and natural. Many practitioners around the world are trained in these techniques and provide them with consistent success to patients and clients.

Effective Treatments

Thought Field Therapy (TFT) is a powerful treatment for dealing with psychological disturbances. TFT provides a code that, when applied to a psychological problem the individual is experiencing, eliminates *perturbations* in the thought field that are the fundamental cause of all negative emotions. A perturbation is a disturbance in the encoding of information that connects a thought with a feeling. TFT acts upon these perturbations to collapse them and render them inactive. Voice Technology is a very advanced form of TFT that uses the human voice to determine the codes that keep anxiety and other negative emotions in place.

I test the person's voice and, using the revealed information, prescribe tapping sequences that the person self-administers on his or her own body. In a matter of minutes, the anxiety and other negative feelings disappear! This procedure works 97 percent of the time and can even be done over the phone.

In cases involving phobias or trauma-based anxiety, one or two treatments are often sufficient to eliminate the anxiety and keep it at bay. Some people need more treatment, and a significant percentage of these people are sensitive to *individual energy toxins*—foods, supplements, toiletries, materials—that they encounter regularly without knowing that these contribute to and trigger anxiety. By voice-testing for toxins, patients are empowered to identify and avoid substances that can trigger anxiety.

Self-help versions of TFT enable many people to effectively treat their own anxiety (See Steinberg, *Living Intact: Challenge and Choice in Tough Times* (2011) for a fuller description and step-by-step self-help guide. My website also provides instruction in these self-help techniques. (See www.marksteinberg.com).

As you will see (in Chapter 8) there are three levels of treatment in TFT: algorithms, causal diagnosis, and Voice Technology.

Algorithms are "summary recipes" for administering TFT that have resulted from applying the commonalities of thousands of individually diagnosed perturbation sequences. Algorithms are what non-professionals typically use to treat themselves (finger tapping, etc.).

Causal diagnosis is the objective scientific procedure of identifying perturbations (specific to particular thought fields) and determining which tapping points and in what order will be most effective in *collapsing the perturbations*—that is, decoding or deprogramming the thought field so that the perturbations that cause the disturbance are no longer active.

Causal diagnosis involves a combination of having the person *attune* the thought field and then using variations of applied kinesiology (muscle testing) to identify the active perturbations. The practitioner typically does this by "testing" various points on the patient's body.

Voice Technology (VT) is the practice of diagnosing the points through information provided by the person's voice. This is the most advanced level of TFT, and it offers a number of advantages including the obvious expediency of treating someone effectively by phone. Voice Technology is also quicker and often more precise in treating patients with greater complexity or long strings of perturbations. VT is also expedient in the identification of toxins that may cause psychological reversals and interfere with treatment. Toxins, the substances that cause a psychological reversal and may block or reverse the effects of successful treatment, typically include various foods, toiletries, aromas, and supplements that act are toxic to a percentage of people. For many, the sustained positive effects of treatments and better health require the identification of and abstention from toxins.

Nature encodes the sources of distress and their solutions within our bodies and minds. Because of nature's recapitulation and signaling system, the human voice indicates with precision the causes of emotional and physical disturbance and can be used in tandem with Thought Field Therapy to eliminate the source and symptoms in minutes.

EEG Neurofeedback is a highly effective method of gradually reducing anxiety and training the brain and nervous system to remain calm even in the face of provocation. Using this method, patients train their brainwaves using computers. This process takes advantage of the brain's natural neuroplasticity by providing feedback. That feedback allows the person to alter the brain's flexibility for integrating the timing mechanisms underlying states of arousal, self-regulation, and the sensations and control of emotions and physiological states.

Neurofeedback is essentially a brain exercise that has pervasive and lasting effects. It enables the brain to find, develop, and restore its own "comfort" levels for maintaining calmness and equanimity. Neurofeedback is effectively used for many conditions. Because it directly influences nervous system control, it almost always enables the reduction of anxiety and exerts a calming influence on the nervous system. After a training regimen, the brain continues to exercise the control it has learned. Anxiety is brought benignly to noninterference levels because the brain learns to maintain self-regulation.

I use a combination of these treatment methods to achieve rapid and lasting effects in the elimination of anxiety. These treatments are natural, effective, and enduring because they address the root causes of anxiety.

Not a Cure for All Your Problems. . . But. . .

The promise of nondrug effective treatments for anxiety-related conditions is a bold and big one. Reading or hearing about this may arouse hope, excitement, and skepticism. We learn to be cautious about believing or embracing solutions that promise life-changing results. Many of these offerings are exaggerated or even deceptive. A combination of hope, anticipation, desperation, disappointments, and cynicism (remembering the already conditioned negative mindset) may provoke interest, disbelief, and high expectations.

The promise I tout delivers great outcomes. Thousands of patients and millions of sessions attest to positive empirical results, provided by different practitioners to diverse populations. Though life doesn't recede with its adversity and challenges, overcoming anxiety and being able to peacefully control your mind goes a very long way toward health, happiness, and long-awaited relief from suffering.

By extolling these treatments, I expose myself to skepticism, criticism, and (perhaps more seriously) fantastic expectations by seekers that quelling their anxiety will make life what they want it to be. Surely this is not the case, as we have all discovered through experience and maturity. Even when things get a lot better, we all have constant hurdles, setbacks, and annoyances. No one can promise a trouble-free life or enduring health without problems. Therefore, I tread carefully along the delicate balance between boldly asserting and backing these treatments that work and knowing that some people will be disappointed, and many others (despite being significantly helped and improved) will continue to be dissatisfied with themselves and what life offers them.

As I shared at the outset, my intent for this book is to shed light on how to get rid of anxiety, as well as how to live with it when it cannot be entirely eliminated. I want to validate these difficult struggles and avoid pie-in-the-sky promises or aspirations to eliminate anxiety entirely. Life is not pain-free, physically or emotionally. Much can be done to live without anxiety; but it's prudent to acknowledge the necessity of tolerating some anxiety—minimizing it substantially, and learning to live more happily with what won't go away. That premise is an important foundation of my message in this book.

CHAPTER 7

Trauma: Roots and Thickets of Anxiety

Relive, Reveal, Release, Resolve

Our minds are capable of many feats that help us survive. We remember the past and use experiences to understand, adapt, plan, and prepare. We interpret the present and assimilate perceptions, events, and feelings into our *schema*, our maps of the world. We anticipate the future and formulate our responses to expectations of what will unfold.

Unfortunately, our impressionable minds are also sensitive and susceptible to retaining and magnifying experiences that are harmful or threatening. Along with our mental and somatic (body) memories of pain and danger, our minds tend to exaggerate, magnify, and catastrophize what *might* happen. Consider the following saying from Mark Twain: "I'm an old man, and I've seen many horrible, terrible, awful things—only most of them never happened."

And this venerable Yiddish adage: *Vos der mensch ken alts iber-trachten, ken der ergster soyna im nisht vinchen.* (What people can think up for themselves, their own worst enemies couldn't wish upon them.)

We all recognize our inherent capacity to dream up and/or exaggerate fears or hypothetical expectations of misfortune or disaster. For some, it is an occasional pang of anxiety and speculation; for others, it becomes an obsessive way of life. The mixture of actual misfortune or trauma with imagined potential often confuses or tricks the mind. Unfortunately, many bad things do happen, and our bodies and minds store these events in emotional and physical memory. This continuation of the damaging memory and experience implants the foundation for a myriad of problems. It is the foundation of traumatic reactions.

Traumatic memory is the essential organizing principle for the majority of psychological distress: anxiety, fear, depression, flashbacks, disordered thinking, sleep disruption, and many others. To effectively deal with traumas, it is helpful to understand the concept of an *organizing principle*.

Essential Organizing Principles

An organizing principle is a core assumption from which everything else, by proximity, can derive a classification or value. This is like a central reference point that allows all other objects to be located, often used in a conceptual framework. Let's take a simple example of how an essential organizing principle that operates when we easily recognize an animal as a dog.

From an early age, any child can learn to recognize a dog—despite the many varieties of dogs and the fact that there are breeds and appearances of dogs that a viewer has never seen in person. Dogs have an essential organizing principle that our minds instantly recognize as belonging to the category of *canine*. When shown a picture of a great Dane, no one will mistake it for a horse or pony, even though they may be similar in size. When looking at a Chihuahua, no one will mistake it for a cat. This is obvious because we have a learned concept of the essential organizing principle of canine that transcends the many individual variations. It is automatic, natural, and a bit hard to define.

Now imagine trying to describe to a Martian (who has never seen a dog) how to recognize a dog. If we say it has four legs and a tail, the Martian—without the reference of essential organizing principle—could easily think that cats or horses are examples of dogs. If we say that a dog barks, the uninitiated may think that a seal is a dog. Just as there are big dogs, small dogs, ones with long fur and those with almost none, particular observable and variable attributes do not uncover the essential organizing principle of *dogness*. And yet, something in our minds and experiences allows us to easily distinguish dogs from other mammals with some shared attributes. Something essential identifies and distinguishes canines from other animals.

We use essential organizing principles constantly to make sense of the world. Typically, this is not a conscious process unless we make a deliberate and orderly practice of critical thinking directed for some logical purpose. This powerful survival tool, however, can also go haywire and lead us astray into false assumptions, inaccurate beliefs, and detrimental lingering emotions. This is what happens when trauma occurs: the emotional brain extends, miscalculates, and misapplies overreacting negative emotions and perceptions to situations (real or imagined) that trigger memories of painful experiences.

Most psychological distress is constructed and continued around the essential organizing principle of trauma. The manifestations are not always recognizable as connected with traumas. Nonetheless, they evoke strong and often overpowering negative feelings. In traumatic *perseveration*—the continuing response to a past event that is no longer present, relevant, or related to current or imagined events, the essential organizing principle of the past trauma evokes a visceral negative response that is inappropriate to current reality. In this process, the emotional mind invokes an errant essential organizing principle upon the object triggering distress. A person with a fear of dogs may have a previous bad experience that originated their fear. However, the same person would not be afraid of a table with four legs!

This subconscious process of projection arises from a mutated template of an inappropriately adapted, essential organizing principle of trauma upon events and perceptions that are experienced as the same, or very similar, to what caused the original trauma. Thus, most continuing and recurring negative emotions are unwittingly (and often unconsciously) triggered by past experiences that continue to live as present traumas in the mind. Anxiety, fear, depression, etc., are our brain's way of neurologically protecting us against threat.

To overcome trauma and be free from its relentless stranglehold, we need to break these inappropriate connections that the brain superimposes from past to present and future experiences.

What Is Trauma?

A trauma may result from the following:

- ✓ An injury caused by an extrinsic agent, especially one causing a disturbance in normal functioning.

- ✓ A psychological shock or severe distress from experiencing a disastrous event outside the range of usual experience, such as rape or military combat.

- ✓ A psychological shock or severe distress from experiencing an attack or loss, or a manipulation or taking advantage of one's vulnerability.

- ✓ A disordered psychological or behavioral state resulting from severe mental or emotional stress or physical injury.

- ✓ A violation or a *perceived violation* of a person's familiar ideas about the world and their rights.

The traditional concept of trauma is predicated on an assumption of a catastrophic event outside the range of usual experience. However, trauma encompasses a much broader range of causal situations and is a very common occurrence. *Traumas are universal, and they occur intermittently in everyone's life. Recovering from traumas is necessary for basic physical functioning and mental and emotional health, and can be accomplished routinely by most people* (given the right tools, training, and support).

In order to understand these points, we must start with the assumption that we all have *vulnerabilities*. Vulnerabilities make us physically and psychologically prone to attack and to breakdown from life's events and forces.

As we accumulate experiences and get to know ourselves, we (ideally) identify (and often protect ourselves against) many of our own vulnerabilities. Certain vulnerabilities are genetically coded and specific. Vulnerabilities are the weak links that allow us to become ill or dysfunctional in a myriad of ways. For example, it is well known that particular diseases tend to run in families. A family history of heart disease, diabetes, depression, etc., doesn't determine that we will be afflicted with these conditions, but it does influence the odds that put us at greater statistical risk.

Trauma occurs when we are caught in an "attack" on one of our "weak links," whether the attack was intentional, random, or even *imagined*. The essence of trauma is that it penetrates defenses, seizes upon vulnerability, and leaves us feeling hurt, defenseless, and usually causes us to "relive" in some way the embedded traumatic experience. Common sense observation and our own experiences will confirm this cause-and-effect link.

After a vehicle accident or near-accident, many people habitually tend to tense up when reminders or even vaguely similar conditions present themselves, as if girding up for another accident. For example, suppose you were in an auto accident that really rattled you, perhaps even injured you. For a long time afterward, you might become anxious when approaching the scene of that accident. Or say the police were pursuing a speeding car that blew through a red light and almost hit your car. Subsequently, you might panic whenever you hear in the distance the sound of a police siren while you are driving. This reaction evokes physiological (fight-or-flight) as well as psychological / mental / emotional responses. The set of defensive responses to an anticipated offending event (in the absence of its presence or direct evidence that it will necessarily occur) is called *perseveration*: responding to an event that is no longer present.

Many forms of trauma occur when people are subjected to harsh conditions, abuse, overwhelming negativity, rejection, racism, isolation, poverty, and so forth. For many people however, it is overwhelming enough even to have to deal with the more mundane traumas that result from the daily interactions, demands, and conflicts typically associated with *ordinary relationships*.

When a spouse, boss, friend, child, relative, partner, teammate, peer does not react in the way we want or expect, it can be emotionally traumatic. We need not be oversensitive or even know that the trauma is occurring. We can, however, tell by the aftereffects. Remember: the nature of trauma is that it causes us to relive or anticipate an event or reaction that previously left us hurt, shocked, exposed, or defenseless. So when we find ourself (or our relationship partner) revisiting the same conflicts, scripts, and (quickly accelerated) emotional responses to the faintest of cues, we will know that a trauma has been incited and activated.

For these traumas, we don't need access to an emergency room or enter years of therapy. What we do need is the realization that we are probably reacting to some provocation that stimulates a less-than-conscious, unresolved emotional vulnerability that initiated a trauma. Such awareness will enable us to see our inner responses and our outward behavior as reactions to a trauma that we may perceive viscerally as necessary, but are neither a function of choice and clear thinking, nor conducive to planning, keen observation, evaluation, or problem-solving.

Medical Study on Adverse Childhood Experience and Health

A large-scale study headed by physicians Vincent Felitti and Robert Anda examined the relationships of adverse childhood experiences with disease in adulthood. Their study found significant correlations between adverse childhood experiences and incidences of obesity, heart disease, drug abuse, smoking, depression, anxiety, suicide attempts, sexually transmitted diseases, cancer, diabetes, traumatic brain injury, overall poor health, and early death. This study (known as the CDC-Kaiser Study "Relationship of Childhood Abuse and Household Dysfunction to Many of the Leading Causes of Death in Adults") included over 17,000 Kaiser patients.

Among the striking findings from the research was the link between mental health precursors in childhood and the development of physical, life-threatening illnesses in adulthood. This marshals quite a challenge to the attitude that "it's all in your head." Statistically, it's in our body—literally—and wreaking havoc consequentially with our health and longevity.

The basis for the study was correlations between scores on a self-reported instrument of childhood experiences and adverse adult health conditions. The instrument used for patient reports is called the Adverse Childhood Experience Test. This self-report is based upon individual recollections and answers to ten questions:

Adverse Childhood Experience (ACE) Questionnaire

DURING YOUR FIRST 18 YEARS OF LIFE . . .	YES	NO
1. Did a parent or other adult in the household **often** swear at you, insult you, put you down, or humiliate you, **or** act in a way that made you afraid that you might be physically hurt?	☐	☐
2. Did a parent or other adult in the household **often** push, grab, slap, or throw something at you, **or ever** hit you so hard that you had marks or were injured?	☐	☐
3. Did an adult or person at least five years older than you **ever** touch or fondle you, or have you touch their body in a sexual way **or** try to or actually have oral, anal, or vaginal sex with you?	☐	☐
4. Did you **often** feel that no one in your family loved you or thought you were important or special **or** that your family didn't look out for each other, feel close to each other, or support each other?	☐	☐

DURING YOUR FIRST 18 YEARS OF LIFE . . .	YES	NO
5. Did you **often** feel that you didn't have enough to eat, had to wear dirty clothes, and had no one to protect you, **or** that your parents were too drunk or high to take care of you or take you to the doctor if you needed it?	☐	☐
6. Were your parents **ever** separated or divorced?	☐	☐
7. Was your mother/stepmother **often** pushed, grabbed, slapped, or had some- thing thrown at her **or sometimes or often** kicked, bitten, hit with a fist, or hit with something hard, **or ever** repeatedly hit over (at least) a few minutes or threatened with a gun or knife?	☐	☐
8. Did you live with anyone who was a problem drinker or alcoholic or who used street drugs?	☐	☐
9. Was a household member depressed or mentally ill, and/or ever attempt suicide?	☐	☐
10. Did a household member ever go to prison?	☐	☐
Add the number of YES answers to see your ACE score	____	____

What the ACE Score Means

An ACE score is a tally of different types of abuse, neglect, and other hallmarks of a rough childhood. According to the Adverse Childhood Experiences study, the rougher one's childhood, the higher the score is likely to be, and the higher the risk for later health problems.

According to the study results, a tally score of greater than 2, regardless of which questions were endorsed with "yes," is highly correlated with adverse health outcomes in adulthood. The greater the number of "yes" scores, the stronger the correlation. Scores of 4 or higher were strongly correlated with incidences of adult health problems.

Persons who experienced four or more categories of childhood exposure, compared to those who experienced none, had a 4 to 12-fold, increased health risk for alcoholism, drug abuse, depression, and suicide attempt; a 2 to 4-fold increase in smoking, poor self-rated health > or = fifty sexual intercourse partners, and sexually transmitted disease; and 1.4 to 1.6-fold increase in physical inactivity and severe obesity.

The link between ACE scores and physical and psychological problems is correlational. That is, a significant statistical probability exists in the relationship between childhood trauma and predicted negative outcomes. This correlation is grounds for the assumption of a high-risk factor for those with such a history.

So what can you or I do—and what can we all do as a society—to mitigate the effects of early adverse experiences? Let's explore the various traumas people endure and some relevant steps to overcoming the negative impact and nightmares of trauma.

Types of Trauma

Traumas occur in many forms and variations:

Physical trauma: Our bodies (nerves and muscles) store memories of impact and hurt. Accidents, illnesses, injuries, assaults, medical procedures, and the unintended effects of medicines can cause the body and brain to respond in a defensive and overprotect mode. Such somatic records can surface for many years in the form of chronic pain.

Emotional trauma: The lasting and devastating effect of a traumatic experience upon our feelings is the archetype of the painful impact that we carry across time and circumstances. Emotional trauma is at the root of posttraumatic stress disorder.

Environmental trauma: Natural disasters such as floods, fires, chemical leaks, and many other events can cause lasting physical, financial, and emotional damage. Being forced to move or uproot can produce trauma. Consider the tragedy of homelessness.

Social/political trauma: One has only to look at the political and social divisiveness throughout the world to observe many sources of traumatic impact. The historical continuity of "man's inhumanity to man" through war, oppression, violence, racism, and so forth, attests to the epigenetic (and spiritual) effects of one's need to dominate, control, and acquire at the expense of others.

Social/personal trauma: Many traumas are associated with experiences of deprivation, betrayal, and unmet needs. Among these are infidelity, scams, and all kinds of rejection, thwarting of goals, and disappointments. Rape, aggression, bullying, stalking, and cyber intrusions cause traumas. Tragically, many people have lived through war and other politically induced traumas. Emigrating to a new country with its adjustments, challenges, and attendant difficulties in learning the language and customs also can be traumatizing.

Family trauma: The family "should" be a protective haven that provides protection, security, love, material needs, and nurture our development and confidence. Though all families are dysfunctional to some degree, many are clearly nightmares of dysfunction and abuse. Even in the most wholesome of environments, the rigors and challenges of growing up can nonetheless produce trauma.

Developmental trauma: Developmental trauma comprises a host of normal and excessive challenges that are necessary to develop life skills, but that can also carry traumatic side effects. The processes and stages of growing up necessitate finding one's own skills and identity (a decades-long progression), competing against others, and becoming as independent as one's resources allow. A natural process of *desatellization* occurs as one matures. Desatellization (in the psychological sense) refers to breaking free from the "gravitational" orbit of one's parents or family of origin. This includes developing emotional and economic independence while retaining adaptive attachments; and reconciling conflicts, unmet needs, and accepting the limitations of the elders projected as all-powerful in the childhood mind. Obstacles in this elongated process can result in various traumas and stunted psychological growth, sometimes called arrested development.

Microtrauma: Emotional wounds caused by repeated situational events or impressions trigger sensitivities. These microtraumas can result when people are subject to harassment. insults, mockery, or negative insinuations by others.

Core Elements of Stopping Trauma Impact

Traumas happen to everyone. They may be individually unpredictable, but they are unavoidable, as each of us undergoes adversity that can have prolonged impact. This impact, however, can be mitigated, healed, and resolved. Four stages occur in the elimination of trauma:

1. Relive

By their very nature, traumas compel victims to relive the traumatic event repeatedly, sometimes without apparent provocation, and often with triggers that bring back the emotional terror as though the event is occurring continuously. Such restimulations, consciously connected or not, produce pain, shock, panic, and overwhelming distress. The trauma resurfaces with vengeance, inducing the overwhelming sense of vulnerability, helplessness, and threat.

We sometimes refer to recurring traumatic feelings as "encapsulated traumas." This means that the memories, sensations, and feelings are isolated from the normal functioning of the brain and nervous system. This encapsulation protects the rest of the system from becoming completely overwhelmed and unable to function.

This is the neuropsychological equivalent of white blood cells surrounding microbial invaders, so the fight for conquest on behalf of the immune system can occur apart from threat and involvement with the rest of metabolic functions. This "back alley" brawl is nature's way of protecting and battling against the threat. But a cost to the system is typically experienced in the nightmarish symptoms of reliving the event.

2. Reveal

Trauma manifests in multiple ways. In many cases, the person is cognizant of the trauma and consciously relives (despite trying to forget) the event. This may occur as flashbacks, nightmares, loose or tangential thought associations, and the attendant visceral response of heightened arousal and fight-or-fight reaction.

The reemergence of traumatic response is visceral, regardless of whether it is attached to conscious memories. Its jarring effect elicits attention and fear, prompting reinforcement of heightened nervous system alert and a generalization to suspect and avoid stimuli and situations reminiscent of the trauma. This builds the habit of fear, uncertainty, lowered confidence, and general anxious anticipation of what might trigger another reaction.

Trauma can reveal itself as explicit painful memories, or it can show up in chameleon representations of varied psychological symptoms. Negative emotions (anxiety, depression, panic, anger, etc.), self-regulation disruptions (attention, concentration, sleep), motivational decay, and somatic disturbances can reflect the core essential organizing principle of trauma that is the linchpin for these emotional and behavioral symptoms. Recurring reminders, such as microtraumas, can remind and again instigate the nervous system to posttraumatic responses.

In cases where no obvious or conscious cause connects the trauma to present distress, it's not necessary to search for the buried or repressed event. Trauma can be healed without regression or bringing to the conscious mind what may have caused it. What's important is to understand that persistent symptoms are perseverative continuations (and sometimes metastatic variations) of originating traumas.

Anxiety and depression have many sources, and the physiological and neurological habits that sustain them can arise and develop from causes beyond trauma. However, the converse informs us that unresolved trauma necessarily produces manifestations of psychological distress.

Consider these analogies: auditory processing disorders can occur as a consequence of different brain patterns and deficits, even in the absence of organic hearing loss. However, measurable physical hearing loss almost certainly causes some degree of auditory processing deficits. You can have a stomachache without a determinable medical cause. But if you have ulcers or cancer, you will definitely have symptoms directly traceable to the cause.

By assuming that persistent psychological distress reflects underlying trauma, it's possible to treat the surface symptoms and the originating stimulus without knowing or even targeting the instigating event. The presenting symptoms reveal the maladaptive response, as well as the essential organizing principle of the body/mind's response to previous trauma.

3. Release

The healing component of traumatic cycles involves releasing the person from the continuing grip of the perseverative trauma. This is the work of trauma therapy with the goal of mental, emotional, and spiritual freedom. Release requires defusing and disconnecting negative emotional responses from the history that launched them. As stated, this can be done with or without conscious or specific associations with the event.

Effective release results in the abatement of persisting symptoms, and the ability to recall aversive events without negative emotions or the habit of obsessing or dwelling on the event. This happens when the emotional fusion with the trauma is separated. It's as though a rattling alarm in the brain has been turned off. When traumatic response is eliminated, an accompanying breadth of emotional range and flexibility results. Freed from the stranglehold of emotional compulsion and constriction, the person experiences more consonance with present circumstances. That is, feelings come more naturally and harmoniously, and more often *fit* appropriately and functionally with imminent situations.

When trauma is released, the brain can better assimilate and accommodate new experiences and assess them realistically without the throwbacks triggered by the trauma.

4. Resolve

To resolve is to finish something, to bring it to conclusion. When we are truly done with something, there's no need to keep revisiting it, despite its potential consequences.

Resolving traumas means we are done with them. They stop haunting us and occupying our defenses. Traumas are historical and may have lasting consequences, but resolution means that our body and brain have healed adequately enough that the trauma is no longer causing issues.

The resolution process does not require "reframing" the traumatic event in order to reduce emotional pain or dissonance. Effective trauma treatment accomplishes that. Resolution involves integrating the "new self"—without the persisting symptoms—with the freedom and growth that follows release. Over time, and perhaps with coaching and improved relationships, one learns to "fit" the terrible misfortune in with one's life development and evolution. Memories are revised to incorporate how one overcame and adapted. The impact of the trauma is rescripted into one's history without the overwhelming tinge of fear and damage. Wholeness tends to pervade and color memory more favorably.

Once trauma is resolved, it's likely that confidence and resilience will be restored and enhanced.

Trauma Be Gone

Over decades of clinical work with patients, I have treated trauma in its many forms, both overt and in its disguises. Before I recognized the relevance of trauma as an essential organizing principle of various psychological symptoms and conditions, I treated them as separate entities. Nonetheless, I've had increasing and consistent success using the advanced techniques of EEG neurofeedback and Voice Technology.

Discerning the core relevance of trauma has made treatment success more rapid and pervasively applicable to broader conditions that were once thought to be beyond efficacy with therapeutic methods.

It's increasingly apparent to veteran practitioners, using these (and other) techniques to heal trauma, that effective healing bypasses conscious processing and thought patterns, and defuses and separates the connections between past experiences and persistent negative emotions. By training the brain and nervous system to invoke and develop more functional patterns of neurological self-regulation, there evolves an automatic reduction of hypervigilance and dysfunctional arousal. These advanced, natural, and organic treatment methods allow and facilitate the brain to heal itself and to disengage the internal alarm system that fires without critical danger.

When traumas are healed (put to rest, resolved, left behind), victims are no longer victims continuing to suffer its effects. Most importantly, symptoms abate and stop inflicting pain and restriction. Resilience and rejuvenation emerge. A modest resurgence of innocence can occur in the sense that one no longer feels damaged or shamed. The ability to trust is renewed. Trauma release and resolution bequeaths a sense of emotional freedom, wholeness, and improved well-being.

Living without the shackles of emotional prison facilitates the development of confidence, security, and the belief that the world can be a safe and manageable place, despite the reality of sin and danger.

CHAPTER 8

Anxiety and Conscience

Overwrought, persistent anxiety detracts from health and happiness, and afflicts millions upon millions of people. We all have periods of exacerbated stress and times when everything piles up and overwhelms. For many however, anxiety is a constant nemesis, invading the inner mind and relentlessly tormenting the emotions, thoughts, spirit, and body.

Intense and recurrent anxiety is an aberration of the central nervous system response to demands made from the environment and a person's perceptions or threat of danger (actual or suspected). In general, excess anxiety is maladaptive and detrimental.

However there are adaptive positive aspects of anxiety that serve purposes for individual and collective survival. Among these adaptive qualities is the role of anxiety in collaborating with conscience.

The concept of "conscience," as commonly referred to in its moral sense, is the inherent ability of a healthy human being to perceive what is right and what is wrong and, on the strength of this perception, to control, monitor, evaluate, and execute their actions. Conscience involves an inner feeling or voice acting as a guide to the rightness or wrongness of one's behavior.

Conscience depends upon measurement of whether one's behaviors and impulses conform to their own standards of right and wrong. These standards may vary according to one's values and religious or cultural precepts. Nonetheless, whatever standards with which they are judged, conscience invokes the concept and actuality of *guilt*. Conscience nags when one feels or believes oneself to be guilty.

Basis of Conscience

The presumption of a conscience—an inner awareness of thoughts and feelings in regard to one's desires and behaviors—depends upon standards of right and wrong. Everyone has standards of right and wrong, even though these may vary widely according to beliefs, social mores, and laws. Arguably for some extremely self-centered people, right and wrong centers around their egotistical concerns and justifications about what they want to do. Nonetheless, everyone uses some standards to differentiate between right and wrong and to draw lines demarcating what's okay and what's not.[8]

Conscience comes into play when one is aware of their own behaviors that cross the line into the domain of wrongness. Conscience invokes a number of negative feelings, such as shame, embarrassment, self-loathing. But the principal negative feeling that drives conscience is *fear*—the palpable anxiety of being found out, exposed, and possibly punished for one's transgressions. Fear is a primal emotion that we need for survival. It can also extend into projected or imaginal scenarios that instigate a threat (perceived or actual). When bothered by conscience, one has a sense of guilt about doing or wanting to do something wrong.

For people severely lacking in compassion or empathy, concerns about right and wrong may be pathologically limited to fear of being caught and calculated assessments of such likelihood. For them, the anxiety is not coupled with remorse, but is constrained to the fear of punishment. Censure matters only to the degree it's accompanied by harsh penalties.

The rest of us rely upon more social, moral, and perhaps spiritual accords to define and include in our boundaries of what is acceptable, specifically what is *right*. Deviating from the standards one applies results in anxiety and fear. Thus the anxiety brought on by pangs of conscience necessarily involves the awareness of guilt.

---

8. Ironically, even criminals who may justify their stealing object to others stealing from them!

Discussions about guilt are difficult and highly sensitive. They arouse ambivalence, past traumas, previous conditioning, and often defensiveness. None of us like to be made aware of our mistakes, poor choices, failures, and the disapproval or censure by others. Moral values, religious convictions, and cultural and family traditions may contribute to allegations, condemnation, sanctions, and even ostracism. So it is a risky business to assert one's position regarding the ethics and boundaries of right and wrong.

A place to start in gaining a foothold on right and wrong is to distinguish the precepts according to whether one views right and wrong as *relative* or *absolute*. This distinction is critical because it necessitates a frame of reference for such evaluation and determination.

A relative view of right and wrong takes into account worldly circumstance, context, precedent, history, and assumptions about personal preferences and freedoms. The belief that rightness or acceptability depends upon observed or implied infringement underlies this point of view: *As long as I'm not hurting anyone, what I do should be my business, free from outside interference or sanctions.* This position is foundational in a secular world.

The opposing and incompatible position holds that there is absolute truth and inviolable standards for right and wrong, and that these are knowable and independent of individual desires and opinions. To say, "the devil is in the details" is a wry understatement of the murky territory that accompanies beliefs about right and wrong regarding religion, taboos, and spiritual and man-made laws.

The purpose of bringing this up is to underscore the relevance of beliefs, standards, and boundaries in illuminating how conscience and anxiety are intertwined and to stimulate awareness in the mind's connections and responses in the interest of diminishing anxiety. Realizing that I navigate a tricky and hazardous landscape of opinions, convictions, and dogma, I nevertheless think that straightforwardness and sensitivity should accompany a candid disclosure of my stance on this issue.

I am adamantly in the camp of belief in absolute truth (which doesn't mean that I am in possession of it, nor that I have any *right* to impose my beliefs on those who sustain other views). I believe that truth and right and wrong are determined by God, and that they are knowable and interpretable by discernment of and receptivity to God's standards. As a follower of Christ, I have chosen a path of using the Bible as the arbiter of truth and rightness. It is my practice and lifestyle to study and aspire to living according to biblical wisdom and instruction. This is a joyous, though troubling lifetime venture of self-assessment, pretense, defensiveness, pleading battle between selfishness and virtue, pride and humility that play out in my life.

I assert my beliefs boldly, wanting and hoping that intellectual clarity and spiritual bravery will respectfully underpin my professional knowledge to help others—and especially those afflicted with anxiety—use this information to live happier and more useful lives. After all, that is the purpose of this book.

My explanation of the inseparability of conscience from guilt and forgiveness is aimed at helping people navigate a healing path, traversing conscience and anxiety, one that is consonant with each person's experience and trust.

Bearing in mind the roots and causes of anxiety explained in previous chapters, we engender the aspect of anxiety that derives from remorse or wrongful behavior (subjective and objective), and we delve into the imbroglio of guilt and forgiveness as components of anxiety and means of its dissuading it.

Guilt and Forgiveness

We live in a world governed by rules, procedures, and laws. In addition to the laws of nature are the laws of man and the laws of God. Failure to heed the laws of nature can have dire consequences. (Consider the saying, "Gravity doesn't care.")

Breaking the laws of man (such as civil and criminal codes of conduct) can bring sanctions and penalties. And disobedience to God's laws results in sin and its attendant outcomes (guilt, separation from God, brokenness.). Guilt without forgiveness demands payment. Sadly, most of us are more familiar with guilt than with forgiveness.

Every society and culture has boundaries and taboos. These are established to facilitate the peaceful and productive functioning of communities, protect their property and people, and preserve their traditions and the sanctity of life. Sometimes, we may seemingly "get away" with transgressions, escape external consequences, and transcend internal conflict; but in the end, we must sooner or later answer to three judges: God (and God's natural laws), society's laws, and our conscience.

> *All who sin apart from the law will also perish apart from the law, and all who sin under the law will be judged by the law.* (Romans 2:12)

> *The sins of some men are obvious, reaching the place of judgment ahead of them; the sins of others trail behind them. In the same way, good deeds are obvious, and even those that are not cannot be hidden.* (1 Timothy 5:24–25)

Living compassionately and responsibly requires regulating a balance among states of mind and the conditions, based on the tangible facts that constitute reality. To live responsibly in the world that *is*, rather than in an illusory world designed to conform to and perpetuate our comfort level, we must inevitably deal with boundaries, violations, and consequences. This accountability creates the context for having to "pay the piper" at some point, and to experience guilt.

Guilt as a Duality

Guilt is an actuality, as well as a state of mind.

As an actuality, guilt is the fact or occurrence of doing something wrong—a violation or transgression of boundaries or rules.

As a state of mind, guilt is an awareness of having done, wanting to do, or thinking about doing something wrong—that is, a violation or transgression of boundaries or rules. Guilt is typically accompanied by feelings of shame and regret.

To be guilty is to have done something wrong, transgressed a boundary, or violated a rule or law. Guilt is contingent upon our being able to objectively differentiate right from wrong. We can be guilty of breaking the law, cheating at a game or in a relationship, and even of violating our own self-imposed limits. In a world of relativity—where "you do your thing, and I do mine"—there can be no guilt because guilt depends upon absolutes, clearly defined parameters of what is allowed and what is not allowed. In practice, guilt is determined by subjection to a law, a rule, or a commonly accepted standard.

As a state of mind or an emotion (more aptly, a state of *heart*), guilt may or may not be aligned with a judgment of culpability that is rendered based upon facts and evidence. You can also *feel* guilty, irrespective of the facts and evidence, and irrespective of whether or not others see or agree with your perceptions of events that have transpired. (God, of course, sees everything that goes on, including your feelings, though God may not agree with you about them.)

We are reminded of sanctions and prohibitions, instructions, and guidelines at every turn: obey the speed limit, do your work, pay what you owe, leash your dog, recycle, use less gas and electric, eat healthier foods, and so forth. If we disobey the rules, we may suffer from the criticism of others and from pangs of conscience triggered by our inner narrative.

Guilt can be a double-sided blade. When we experience it, we are often distressed by the negative feeling, as well as by the guilt associated with believing we deserve to experience negative emotions because of our "evilness." Moreover, we can also be burdened by the guilt of having to struggle with and obsess about our own tendencies to have negative thoughts.

Guilt as a Negative Emotion

Guilt is a major instigator of anxiety that ranks high on a list of insidious negative emotions that can rob us of peace of mind and wellness. As in the case with other negative emotions, guilt is an unpleasant state of mind that can be linked to arousal states influenced by perceptions, imagination, or associations with previous experiences. If these arousal states are maintained inappropriately or for extended periods, they will likely seriously impair our capacity to enjoy life.

All negative emotions can have a direct impact on our behavior. The emotions of anger and fear are two of the most notable examples, both of which are also tied to anxiety. Anger can cause us to lash out, and fear can make us withdraw or flee. Though feelings are by nature subjective, they are often rooted in the "real world." We are supposed to be afraid when threatened by a gunman, and we naturally feel embarrassed when we find ourselves in a position that robs us of respect or dignity. In such cases, negative emotions are helpful, *temporary* motivations that provide impetus to repair or exit from a threatening or damaging situation. When the threatening stimulus disappears, the negative emotion usually does too. (traumas and phobias are notable exceptions.)

Guilt, however, is different from other negative emotions in that it can be a *condition* as well as a *feeling*. You can be fearful or sad for good "reason," but you only *feel* that way. You can *be guilty* of a transgression by applying objective standards, regardless of whether or not you actually *feel* guilty. To make matters more confusing, you can *feel* guilty without actually *being guilty*! Here we have a complicated interrelationship where the feeling of guilt can be related to or independent of an objective condition.

Therefore, it is important to distinguish between *true guilt* and *false guilt*.

Guilty? It Depends

As noted, the concept of guilt is one that necessarily depends upon the standards of right and wrong. Guilt involves a violation or transgression of an accepted or imposed societal boundary that delineates right from wrong. When you cross that boundary, you are guilty. The frame of reference clearly matters. What or who establishes the boundary? Certainly, governmental laws that comprise standards by which guilt can be determined apply to everyone. Acknowledgment of a standard does not imply agreement with or approval of that standard—it simply serves to demarcate a boundary that separates guilt from innocence.

For example, I live near a park where I like to exercise my dog. My dog likes to run, and so I often let him off the leash. He's well-trained, and I am respectful of other people's territory and privacy, as well as the social conventions of city life. A city ordinance (clearly posted) says that all dogs must be leashed in the park. I don't like this city ordinance, although I realize it also applies to me and my dog. Usually

I "get away" with violating this ordinance, justifying to myself all the while that it is really okay to let my dogs run as long as they are not bothering anyone. As you might expect however, occasionally there are people in the park who object to my dog (on or off the leash). When these objecting people run from my dog or yell at me, I hurry to leash my dog. My inner narrative denounces them for being unreasonable, angry, dog-phobic, etc., even as I smile or apologize. Fact is though, I am guilty of violating the city ordinance—whether or not I am caught, called on it, or no one notices. My guilt depends upon violating the law, not upon how I feel. I had no say in making this law, though I am civic enough to have a strong opinion about it.

Aside: Interestingly, I don't *feel* guilty about letting my dog off the leash, even though I know I am violating a law. I do feel guilty about not feeling guilty about violating this city ordinance. This conundrum troubles me because my dog needs to run somewhere, I live in a city, and I also need to be considerate and respectful of others.

The Role of Conscience

The feeling of guilt is an awareness of having done something wrong or committed a transgression, accompanied by a feeling of shame and regret.

So what does it mean to feel guilty?

Whether or not a guilty feeling corresponds to a transgression, a guilty feeling always relates to the emergence of *conscience*—the internal sense of right and wrong influencing thoughts, feelings, and actions, and urging us to do right rather than wrong. Our conscience is the compass that directs our narrative to prompts a feeling of guilt.

Though some believe otherwise, the most religious views hold that everyone is born with a conscience, just as everyone is born with a heart. A conscience is God's voice inside us, guiding us (and our narrative) in the true ways of right instead of wrong. Unfortunately, the reminding voice of conscience can be quieted, corrupted, or even extinguished, and our moral compass can be flawed so as to give false readings, until we become dangerously lost. This can happen as a result of deliberate and repeated willful rebellion or through the dulling and warping of one's thinking through substance abuse or corrupting human influences. It also can occur through developmental neglect, whereby the neurological mechanisms for self-soothing do not develop properly, leaving the brain with an impaired or limited capacity for empathy or compassion. A psychological disorder called reactive attachment disorder, in which the failure to develop the capacity for compassion and empathy, is thought to arise from maternal neglect or absence during very early stages of life. This syndrome is common syndrome in children placed in orphanages shortly after birth. EEG neurofeedback is an effective treatment to help such individuals become more emotionally sentient.

Whatever the origin, when the conscience does not perform as God designed, a conspicuous and destructive lack of remorse permits and justifies selfish and dangerous behavior. Extreme examples of this are found in the actions of sociopaths whose antisocial behaviors are marked by crimes with little or no feelings for their victims.

Keeping in mind that the conscience as pivotal, let's differentiate between *true* and *false* guilt.

True Guilt and False Guilt

True guilt is the awareness or existence of a feeling, behavior, or intent related to doing or having done something wrong; and true guilt is usually accompanied by a feeling of anxiety, shame, or regret. True guilt is identified by the *conviction* or *acceptance* that one's actions, feelings, or intentions are *wrong* according to a doctrine of law or truth. True guilt may also be labeled *actual*.

False guilt is also the awareness of a feeling, behavior, or intent accompanied by a feeling of anxiety, shame, or regret, but is distinguished from true guilt by the *absence of a transgression*—that is, false guilt feels like you did or *might do* something wrong, even when you did not commit an actual transgression. False guilt is not "pretend" because, unlike pretending, false guilt carries no recognition that the feeling and its circumstances are make-believe. They seem real and feel real, though they are not. False guilt may also be labeled *imagined*.

The following matrix compares and contrasts the characteristics of and interrelationships among true and false guilt and their associated feelings:

	True Guilt	False Guilt
Feel Guilty	Violation of law or rule Convicted by conscience Remorse and anxiety	No transgression or wrongdoing Powerlessness and anxiety Habitual compulsion
Do Not Feel Guilty	Violation of law or rule Unaware of transgression Lack of remorse	No transgression or wrongdoing No dissonance Non-issue
Believe You Are Guilty	Recognition of actuality Understanding of reality Guided by reason	Lack of true facts Faulty reasoning False assumptions

Guilty Feelings and False Guilt

I have often treated patients who are tormented by the sense of guilt over what they have done or *think* they have done wrong. They review the past, brood and berate themselves, and cannot let go of self-recriminations. Guilty feelings haunt them, and they feel trapped. In many cases, these people have not accurately examined the source of their guilty feelings or the foundation for true guilt, which is actually doing something wrong.

Why do people become stuck in feelings of false guilt? The phenomenon can be attributed to several factors:

1. Anxiety and the role of the narrative in justifying the feelings

2. Faulty reasoning and false assumptions about causality

3. Lack of factual examination supporting actual transgressions

4. Resignation and hopelessness

Let's examine how each of these can underpin sustained feelings and beliefs about guilt in circumstances without actual wrongdoing. A good example of unfounded guilt occurs when someone has been molested or otherwise abused physically and/or psychologically, but they feel ashamed and think they somehow caused the event to occur. In such cases, the person is a victim in reality. However, enduring feelings of false guilt often accompany beliefs about the role the victim has or feels they may have played to elicit or deserve the perpetration.

Anxiety and the role of the narrative in justifying the feelings

Victimization is one instance that precipitates trauma. The nature of trauma is that feelings *perseverate* (continue in the absence of relevant stimuli). That is, the emotional parts of the mind are not time-bound. Thus compelling negative feelings that arose from a trauma may continue as if the trauma were still happening, despite the logic and reality that it is not still actually occurring; the emotional brain carries it over and relives it continually. Such perseveration immobilizes victims in the grip of continuing negative emotions. The narrative intervenes and attempts to "explain" the presence of the trauma by linking the gripping feelings to some rationale and to the dynamic of sequential causality.

Faulty reasoning and false assumptions about causality

Led by the narrative, the victim assumes that they *must* have done something to encourage or facilitate the traumatic event. Perhaps true guilt over past transgressions encroaches, overtaking and contaminating the victim with guilt by associating previous sins and the present traumatic but unrelated event. A person with a guilty conscience may fear punishment and suspect that it has come in the form of the traumatic event. Or perhaps the randomness of danger is so odious and overwhelming that the narrative invents explanations to shield against the peril of vulnerability and helplessness, e.g., *I must have done something to encourage and deserve this or else it could not have possibly happened.*

Lack of factual examination supporting actual transgressions

The victim of sexual assault or other abuse often fails to examine and evaluate objectively whether he or she committed some act of wrongdoing that precipitated the perpetration. Overwhelmed by the crushing burden of guilty feelings, a victim typically needs assistance to sort out the facts from the reactive feelings. Yet the nature of guilt is that the associated shame makes people want to keep it private. Acknowledgment is perceived as admission of culpability, and so the bearer of guilty feelings proceeds with no outlet or input to separate feelings and facts from fiction and solid reasoning.

Resignation and hopelessness

The persistence of false guilt frequently accompanies and validates other negative feelings and beliefs. When sufferers are without hope, they find explanations for the constraints, whether or not such thinking stands the test of reality. Guilty feelings, resignation, and hopelessness form a triad of despair that engender obsessive submission to the tyranny of behavioral compulsions: habits that repeat themselves despite the pain of guilt-ridden victims who feel powerless to break the cycle of their own self-defeating habits. This type of false guilt serves as the distracting preoccupation that suggests: *you are going to do it again.* As might be expected, this induces anxiety.

Habit Guilt

Habit guilt is a false guilt that derives from repeatedly succumbing to undesirable behaviors or habits. This guilt, masquerading as wrongdoing, is the feeling of inevitability that you will commit the same behavior over and over again—usually against yourself. In effect, we rationalize and minimize the inevitability of negative, counterproductive behavior, as in:

"I'm going to have that dessert, even though I shouldn't."

"I hate to nag you, but . . ."

"This is extravagant, but I deserve it."

"I really should exercise; however, I'm tired."

"I haven't cleaned the house in weeks. I will get around to cleaning and straightening the house later."

"I should study more."

It makes sense that there can be overlap between the sense of remorse over "guilty pleasures" (e.g., a second dessert), avoidance, other "shoulds" and "oughts" and actual wrongdoing. The violation of one's own standards and boundaries is certainly cause for concern, as it can impair self-confidence, reliability, and integrity. However, remember that true guilt involves the breaking of an actual law or collectively understood standard. If you break your word (or a promise), feeling guilty is appropriate. But if you fail to exercise or keep to your diet as you had hoped, this does not necessarily qualify as guilt (though you may feel justifiable regret).

Feeling guilty over disappointing yourself or even the expectations of others can also serve as an excuse for continuing certain behaviors. Expressing guilt about a recurrent negative self-indulgence can serve as a palliative and a justification for carrying on with habits that are difficult to break. Such a narrative can be quite adept at protecting you from the impact of failure by admitting to false guilt as a consolation when you fail to meet expectations.[9]

Guilt and Tuna Fish

To determine our guilt and peer through the filters of self-delusion and worldly justification that allow escape, or at least the illusion of it, is not always easy. Many people live without a spiritual faith or the Word of God as a compass. Their only reference point may be their feelings. They have few valid standards against which to judge transgression. In their attempts to flee from self-recrimination and free themselves from negative emotions (including resentments), these people spend their energies refusing to accept any "guilt trips" they perceive to be imposed on them by others.

The problem with this approach to "self-liberation" is that unbridled desire, self-justification, and relativistic truth can easily distort the presence of true guilt. (The only one who can lay guilt upon you is God, and God's conviction is not a "trip," but rather a stark reality.)

In helping some of my patients appreciate the quandary of distinguishing among the types of guilt, and ferreting out actual guilt, I've sometimes used the example of tuna fish. When I was a boy, I ate tuna fish frequently, always in the form of canned tuna mixed with

---

9. 6. This type of guilt is a compensatory attempt to bridge the gap between what you expect and what actually results.

mayonnaise—the way my mother made it for me. Mostly it was StarKist tuna with Hellmann's mayonnaise on Wonder Bread. She called it "tuna salad." Occasionally, I was served a slightly different mash of tuna and mayonnaise on rye bread, and I tolerated this with stoic restraint and self-congratulations on my sense of adventure. Nothing, however, prepared me for the "tuna salad" I was served at the local Greek restaurant.

In the Bronx, where I grew up, neighborhoods had a plethora of restaurants with a variety of ethnic specialties. Most of the "American" restaurants were owned and operated by Greek Americans. I went to one in my neighborhood quite frequently, as it was common for me to eat lunch in a restaurant by myself. My customary meal was a cheeseburger; however, on one occasion, with the nagging voice of my mother in my head, I decided to follow her advice and order something "healthy, like tuna salad." So I did.

When my lunch arrived, I was confused and miffed. Set before me was a large plate adorned with lettuce, tomatoes, a few unfamiliar relishes, and in the middle was a circular mold of something tan and smelly. This was, of course, the tuna, right out of an upended can and situated among the greens on the plate. I was horrified. I complained to the waiter, "There must be a mistake—I ordered tuna salad!"

"Yes, that's tuna salad, kid."

Of course it was. Yet it didn't look anything like the whitish-tan, mashed-with-mayonnaise stuff my mother put between slices of white bread. My stomach was growling, my expectations were confounded, the world was not behaving agreeably, and the tuna I thought I knew was apparently a tricky chameleon.

But tuna is tuna—a fish that swims in the sea, gets caught by man, and is served and processed as food in many different ways. It doesn't always wear a can, look like a round mold, or marry mayonnaise. Nonetheless, it is indeed tuna.

Similarly, guilt is guilt about transgression and wrongdoing, no matter how disguised or dressed up. It may be how we feel or what we've done, or it may be both. True guilt occurs when we violate a rule or law, whether or not we *feel* guilty or *believe* we are guilty. Though our beliefs and feelings are more realistic when they coincide with a factual assessment of what happened, true guilt depends upon transgression. It happens when you are out of step with God.

God created truth, guilt, conscience, and tuna fish. Humans capture, process, and manufacture things to our images and desires. Tuna is tuna, and guilt is guilt, however you dress it up.

Resolving Guilt

Once we understand what guilt really is, the requirements for absolving it are straightforward. It is easy and natural to hide from guilt, but doing so detracts from living intact, results in distance from God, and preserves anxiety. To have faith in and know God is to face guilt and human vulnerability, and to also know *forgiveness*. Without forgiveness, guilt would still exist, but it would be unbearable. Fortunately, the supreme Creator of the universe has put in place the gift of forgiveness. The grace and mercy of forgiveness allows humans to overcome sin—with God's help—and to face reality, on God's terms, with responsibility, humility, and compassion.

The first step, obviously, is to acknowledge our guilt. We must be clear when we are truly guilty of wrongdoing. This requires good reality testing. Add to these a clarification as to whether our guilt is true guilt (based upon transgression) or a chameleon of denial, habit guilt, or anxiety/trauma combined with false assumptions.

When we face the realities of our true transgressions, it is time to confess. This means acknowledging that we have transgressed and are guilty. Oh, how difficult it is to admit that we are not right! But if we are at odds with what we know is wrong, we are nevertheless wrong, because right (like God) is *always* right. We admit our sin to God, and that we are truly sorry for what we have done, that we want God's forgiveness and need God's help in not transgressing again.

The Blessing of Forgiveness

Forgiveness means giving up any and all claims we may have regarding wrongs or perpetrations done to or against us. To forgive is to pardon somebody for mistakes or wrongdoing. When we forgive, the debt is forever canceled. Nothing remains owing on that wrong or transgression.

Note that forgiving does not mean forgetting. Forgiving someone doesn't give us amnesia; but neither does it mean that we continue keeping score. The nature of memory is that emotional memory is different from unemotional memory. We can recall facts or events with varying degrees of accuracy and thoroughness. However, such recollections are not *compelling* in the way that emotional memories can be. Intense emotional memories can evoke preoccupation and obsession when they are negative or traumatic.

When we harbor anger or resentment against someone, or when we feel guilty or ashamed, we can become preoccupied with the uncomfortable or painful thoughts associated with those memories. Forgiveness erases the pain and discomfort.

Many people are unable to forgive. This characteristic often has tragic implications. The inability to forgive eats away at health, happiness, and the quality of relationships and contributions. Lack of forgiveness imposes an unnecessary burden; yet so many people live as if that weren't so. It primarily reflects a spiritual problem, though there are practical anchors that tether the heart. In order to forgive, we must experience how it feels to be absolved. Not having had this experience of absolution deprives us of the correct frame of reference. Compare this to the challenge of learning how to speak if one is deaf. There is no frame of reference or model for how words sound.

Spiritual deafness (or blindness or insensitivity) occurs naturally—it is human nature. Circumstances and events in life can skew development toward dysfunctional patterns with regard to the capacity to experience and model compassion and forgiveness.

Even though we may have had harrowing experiences, perhaps even having suffered abuse, neglect, or trauma that have left us hurt, angry, resentful, or mistrustful, there is a path to healing through forgiveness. First, however, we *must experience* being forgiven. That is a gift God assures and provides.

Being Forgiven

We cannot experience being forgiven unless we know and accept that we are guilty. Being guilty means that we have transgressed. When a person transgresses, there are usually consequences. Sometimes these are harsh, but sometimes they are minimal, such as receiving probation or not having a violation go on your record.

Circumstantial consequences may satisfy the payment for certain transgressions. But paying a minimal price does not necessarily relieve guilt. Getting rid of guilt in the eyes of God and the eyes of man (including our own) requires a spiritual absolution. Feeling or being guilty shackles the conscience and emotional freedom. Only God can release us from the bondage of guilt. And only when you experience this can you truly forgive others.

> *For if you forgive men when they sin against you, your heavenly Father will also forgive you. But if you do not forgive men their sins, your Father will not forgive your sins. (Matthew 6:14–15)*

The Peace of Forgiveness

When we see something wonderful, eat great food, or hear enjoyable music, we naturally want to share it with others—tell them about it, help them find it, and savor their enjoyment. Experiencing forgiveness and wanting to share that joy with others trumps any feeling I have ever had. Beyond the feeling, it can summon miracles.

Forgiving others brings a peace that has no equal. When we forgive, we feel a comfort and refreshment and lightness. We know the freedom from the burden of grudge, anger, and resentment. We feel closer to God and bask in his approval about acting righteously. We delight in the peace that mercy brings forth. Moreover, we feel good about ourself for acting maturely and responsibly. Ironically, you will gain a better sense of control of any situation that has been controlling you because of your own lack of forgiveness. And you will observe more astutely the nature of other people and of human emotions as you wait for God to act in the life of the person you forgave.

Then Peter came to Jesus and asked, "Lord, how many times shall I forgive my brother when he sins against me? Up to seven times?" Jesus answered, "I tell you, not seven times, but seventy-seven times. Therefore, the kingdom of heaven is like a king who wanted to settle accounts with his servants. As he began the settlement, a man who owed him ten thousand talents was brought to him. Since he was not able to pay, the master ordered that he and his wife and his children and all that he had be sold to repay the debt. The servant fell on his knees before him. 'Be patient with me,' he begged, 'and I will pay back everything.' The servant's master took pity on him, canceled the debt and let him go. But when that servant went out, he found one of his fellow servants who owed him a hundred denarii. He grabbed him and began to choke him. 'Pay back what you owe me!' he demanded. His fellow servant fell to his knees and begged him, 'Be patient with me, and I will pay you back.' But he refused. Instead, he went off and had the man thrown into prison until he could pay the debt. When the other servants saw what had happened, they were greatly distressed and went and told their master everything that had happened. Then the master called the servant in. 'You wicked servant,' he said, 'I canceled all that debt of yours because you begged me to. Shouldn't you have had mercy on your fellow servant just as I had on you?' In anger his master turned him over to the jailers to be tortured, until he paid back all he owed. This is how my heavenly Father will treat each of you unless you forgive your brother from your heart." (Matthew 18:21–35)

When you forgive others, you are being obedient to God. When you do not forgive, you are living outside of God's protection and blessing. This provides a foothold for succumbing to spiritual and practical influences that are critical, detrimental, and ungodly. Failure to forgive is tantamount to causing yourself pain.

On the other hand, forgiveness is one of the most unselfish acts you can perform. Forgiveness is often not easy, but it is up to you to take the initiative in forgiving.

Forgiving Others

Let's review what forgiveness involves and then delineate steps to forgiving others.

Forgiveness is the giving up of resentment against someone and the right to get even, no matter what has been done to you. It is the surrendering of the right to hurt someone back. Forgiveness cancels the debt forever.

Lack of forgiveness is the deliberate, willful refusal to give up resentment and asserting the right to "get even" based upon the wrongful idea that somebody needs to pay the debt. In short, lack of forgiveness demands payback. (Ironically, it is the lack of forgiveness that actually demands the payment from you.)

Many people say, "I want to forgive; I simply can't." Or, "How can I forget that terrible thing he did?"

To emphasize again: forgiving does not mean forgetting. It means that the memory is no longer important to your heart and emotional mind.

To overcome the obstacle of a mind and heart that are stuck, I have found TFT tapping to be invaluable (See Chapter 11). I consider it to be a sacrament, actually, given by God to help us in our human frailty and stubbornness that puts resistance (and psychological reversal) in the way of forgiveness.

I wholeheartedly recommend (and use myself) TFT procedures at the slightest hint that forgiveness is not flowing naturally and quickly.

Here are the steps: (Review the TFT procedures shown in my link: https://marksteinberg.com/tapping/?access=granted)

1. State out loud: "I want to be over any and all stubbornness in my heart and obstacles to forgiving (name) for (whatever has been done)." Tap on the side of your hand, and repeat the preceding statement.

2. Follow the algorithm treatment for anxiety, making sure to tap on the side of your hand and under your nose in the prescribed sequences (to correct reversals).

113

3. Acknowledge that you have experienced God's forgiveness.

4. Confess your negative emotions (anger, hostility, bitterness, resentment, rage, etc.)—"This is what I've felt and done. This is my attitude. It is not the right attitude."

5. Acknowledge to God that lack of forgiveness is a violation of his Word and principles

6. Ask God for forgiveness—"Forgive me for my (anger, hostility, bitterness, resentment, rage, etc.) toward (name) for whatever he or she has done. (Be specific.)

7. Ask God for help in forgiving the specific person for the specific act.

8. Declare that the debt is forever canceled for the specific person for the specific act.

9. Thank God for freeing you from the slavery and bondage of being unable to forgive.

10. Pray for the welfare and godliness of the person you just forgave.

Forgiveness is an act of choice, and may be among the most difficult choices you will ever make—and you will need to make it over and over again. Forgiveness exemplifies the Golden Rule. The capacity to forgive will bring you joy and contentment throughout your life as well as incalculable golden opportunities to live a life that is both rewarding and intact.

Forgiveness and Reducing Anxiety

Forgiving regularly, repeatedly, and easily relieves the burden of brooding, keeping score, replaying in our mind various scenarios of offense and retribution, and spinning thoughts needlessly. Forgiving also remedies the self-torment and self-blame that fuels obsessive thinking and compulsive behaviors. Knowing and experiencing forgiveness enables us to forgive ourselves, to let go of unreasonable expectations and perfectionist standards self-imposed.

Relieving Conscience and Anxiety

Our conscience guides us and yet can be an irritating thorn, reminding us of guilt and transgressions. In this way, it is tied to anxiety. Be thankful for and mindful of your conscience. Remember that conscience can be muted, numbed, or disregarded, much to the detriment of integrity and natural consequences.

Those given to sociopathic behaviors (and the gangster cultures that collude with nervous system insensitivity) intentionally try to subdue their consciences—this, tragically, in order to survive their circumstances and somehow live with themselves.

In the comedic satire, *Analyze This*, Robert DeNiro plays a Mafia don who suffers anxiety attacks that force him to visit a psychiatrist. Renowned for his brutality, the mobster is worried about his reputation when he finds himself bursting into tears for no apparent reason. He tries to quell his anxiety for the sake of his sanity and in order to continue his savage acts and protect his reputation. The movie poignantly highlights how anxiety and conscience can pressure us to recognize and correct wrongful behavior.

In its larger context, recurring and persistent anxiety is a debilitating aberration and overextension of nervous system response, associated with troubling thoughts and feelings, that perseverates fight-or-flight states beyond what is necessary for actual threat or survival. Its neurological basis notwithstanding, anxiety that is prompted by conscience should be evaluated and heeded as a warning sign that corrective action through moral and behavioral channels may need to be taken.

A body fever incurs tremendous discomfort. Understandably, it is nature's way of sounding the alarm to protect us and alert us to the need for rapid and appropriate intervention. Anxiety resulting from a valid conscience prong needs similar attention.

A wise friend once told me, "Live your life as though you were in the outer window of Macys."

That's a lofty goal, especially when I consider the skeletons in my closet. But I'm not about to break the window and steal what's inside. For that, I am grateful.

Anxiety, Prayer, and Practicality

To conclude this foray into the spiritual aspects of conscience and anxiety, I want to emphasize a few points.

First, though we all have it, conscience is not a priority for scientific measuring or conclusions. The calibration is internal for each
individual. Disregarding or deceiving conscience subjects us to more
pressure to avoid or suppress natural instincts. Again, this is the part
of anxiety we should value as helpful. The biological causes, responses,
and interventions described should be taken in tandem with the intangible but visceral sense that constitutes conscience. Without doing
so, we become vulnerable to more escapism, intoxication, and other
maladaptive methods to avoid the pain.

Second, by including God and spirituality (my version and beliefs
too), I run the risk of alienating those doubtful, unaffiliated, or critical of such persuasions who may be prone to dismiss me and my recommendations. Sensitive or skeptical readers may suspect or bristle)
that I am trying to convert them. Consider this: If your doctor reminds
you about your metabolic factors, your diet and lifestyle, or sounds the
alarm about health risks while offering solutions—is the doctor trying
to *convert* you?

Third, I share a story about a particular pious family who prayed
often about everything, whose prayer and religious adherence were
paramount. Nonetheless, their misguided adolescent was using drugs
and engaging in rebellious, disrespectful, and destructive behavior.
The parents sought solution and healing through God and doubled
down on prayer, relying only upon God to straighten out the adolescent. That was the sole intervention. One morning, as she was bathing,
the mother discovered a lump on her breast. Alarmed, she prayed continuously until the hour when the doctor's office opened, whereupon
she immediately called for an appointment.

We all must balance practicality along with our spirituality. Relieving anxiety is challenging and often complex. We need to look inward
to face and depose our demons, using the assistance of methods that
work. We also need to recognize and deal with the soul, revealed partly

through the resilient conscience that places the template of right and wrong upon our behavior.

Philosophy and practicality should be partners. As Kierkegaard said, "The society that exalts its philosophers but eschews its plumbers will have both bad philosophy and bad plumbing."

Though he was critical of religion, Kierkegaard pointed out the pragmatism that is vital and should be as important as theory and speculations. Thus, if anxiety surfaces from wrong actions or desires, then repentance and appropriate restitution would be appropriate responses as part of the anxiety solution.

CHAPTER 9

Imposter Syndrome

As we develop from childhood throughout life, we carve our identity and self-image from a variety of interactions with the world and its inhabitants, as well as through discovering and exercising our skills and talents. This evolving process is modified by experiences, feedback, performance, and the values and beliefs we accumulate. New information from life events challenges or confirms previously accommodated views of the self and may beckon adjustment to bring congruence between previous outlook and new experiences.

Our identity—who we think we are and how we are defined by others—is actually comprised of different *selves*: these are roles we assume, masks and pretenses (a normal and necessary aspect of public and private behavior, as well as defense mechanisms), and the images, responses, and attitudes projected by others.

We aspire to achieve a secure and robust identity, and we hope that this identity is resilient, unique, and under our possession and control. However, our identity can be breached and compromised. Caution and discretion are increasingly necessary to guard against criminal theft of identity. Beyond thievery by others of our material possessions and name, our psychological identity is also vulnerable to many influences, including trauma, illness, injury, betrayal, misfortunes, and self-doubt.

While some people are (or seem) very self-confident, and a small percentage of folks are overconfident or even narcissistic, a high percentage of people suffer from lack of confidence or low self-esteem. People who struggle with psychological identity issues put great emotional effort into hiding their insecurities and anxieties. They often feel transparent or exposed, believing or worrying that others can easily see their flaws and deficiencies.

When people think that others may see through their veneer, they experience a distressing incongruence between their projected self and who they think they really are. This experience of discrepancy or false self has become known as *imposter syndrome*—a persistent condition of feeling anxious and not experiencing success internally, despite being high-performing in external, objective ways. The condition often results in people feeling like "a fraud" or "a phony" and doubting their abilities. Imposter syndrome is the persistent inability to believe that one's success is deserved or has been legitimately achieved as a result of one's own efforts or skills.

Fearing that one may be exposed and embarrassed creates intense and persistent anxiety. Bearing in mind that anxiety is a physiological response coupled with (and justified by) thoughts, the triggers or themes of recurring anxiety are incidental to and overshadowed by the physiological onslaught. Nevertheless, imposter syndrome brings into play more basic underlying fears and recapitulating themes of fragmented and fragile identity.

Many Imposters

Movie stars and celebrities are often known to exude the profound need for approval and adulation. Many have extended egos and public persona bravado that mask inner self-doubt.

Surely, the self-doubt and concerns about phony projections are legion among those we admire, as well as among the general public.

A personal example that made a deep impression upon me occurred when my respected therapist in college shared an example of his own traumatic self-doubt. He told me that for months before his graduation from a PhD program, he had a recurring nightmare. Almost every night, he awakened from this same dream in a state of panic and profuse sweating. In the dream, as he walked across the ceremonial stage to receive his diploma, someone in the row stood up and shouted, "NO, not him! He's a fraud! Don't give John a diploma—he doesn't know anything. He's a fake!"

Dr. John recounted this imposter trauma decades after his graduation, and so had time and experience to overcome his fears. He was an excellent, experienced professional, and he brimmed with confidence, reassurance, competence, and empathy. Nonetheless, his report of the trauma and feelings of being an imposter echoed a familiar theme.

It's understandable that someone—any of us—with little experience at some task or role, or at the beginning of an endeavor or career, would likely feel hesitation and uncertainty. Depending upon the situation, stakes, and one's general level of confidence and stability, some degree of anxiety and tension is natural and expected. However, if the novelty of performance and fear of mistakes does not progressively diminish and yield to growing self-assurance, a case of imposter syndrome may be lurking or incipient.

Intentional Imposters

Undesired feelings of being an imposter cause great anxiety. Yet it's prudent to also recognize that posturing or pretending is part of learning and serves great value in development and in art. Actors pretend, of course. Many actors have said that in order to fulfill their roles credibly, they must *inhabit* the persona of their character. Some of this technique is known as *method acting*.

Many children have a natural inclination to don their parents' clothing and act "grown-up." There are even child beauty pageants.

Rookie athletes and neophytes at jobs must assume an air of confidence, even as they are assuming new roles that may be uncomfortable. Sales people must walk a careful line between touting the virtues and importance of their product (and their experience) and truthfully representing what they are selling.

I confess an embarrassing story about being an imposter when I was younger. Early in college, I took a summer job hawking local newspapers by phone. I sat in an office cubicle cold-calling residents in my college town. I represented myself as a priest, saying, "Hello, this is

Father Steinberg, and I'm calling on behalf of the Archdiocese. Will you help our struggling and deserving youth by purchasing a newspaper subscription so we can give young people delivery jobs?"

I admit this was unethical (even sleazy) and likely unlawful, but fifty years ago, I was ambitious and eager to cut my teeth on sales skills and seeing how far my impersonation skills could go.

Note: I did sell newspapers, but am abashed by this activity. Fortunately, I have matured, and am fastidious about representing myself honestly.

Although we might not think of name changes as being imposters, it's also worth noting that many actors, writers, and others have assumed new names to foster a new identity or persona or to hide their ethnicity.

Marilyn Monroe was born Norma Jean Mortenson.

John Wayne was born Marion Robert Morrison.

Mark Twain was the pen name of Samuel Clemens.

Dean Martin changed his birth name, Dino Paul Crocetti

And the list goes on.

Psychological and Personality Masks

In the annals of personality theory, Carl Jung was a great contributor to our understanding of the subconscious influences upon our preferences and behaviors. Jung posited four basic personality types: introverted intuition, extroverted intuition, introverted sensation, and extroverted sensation. Other theorists and developers of assessment tools have expanded upon Jung's work into personality tests and temperament profiles. Among the well-known examples are the Myers-Briggs Type Indicator, Cattell's 16 Personality Factor Test, and the DISC system of personal behavioral styles (dominance, influence, steadiness, and conscientiousness). I've found the DISC system to be especially useful in uncovering and teaching patients' needs and tendencies to help them better understand and avail themselves of coping and modification strategies.

In brief, the expansion of Jungian theory shows that we put on "masks" to display personality styles publicly that often hide, modify, or minimize our "true" selves. For instance, someone with high drive, ambition, or aggressiveness may mask such traits (unwittingly) to soften the tendency to come on too strong. A person with strong needs for approval may modify his external demeanor in order to play down the need for approbation.

Such personality masks are normal aspects of the roles we play (or images we think we should project), and do not in themselves suggest being an imposter. However, it is wise to become aware of one's own inner needs and outward tendencies, and to develop and maintain consonance between the "self" that we feel and own, and the identity we display, intentionally or otherwise, to the world.

Working With Imposter Syndrome

Helping people with deep-seated convictions about their lack of worthiness is a difficult process that requires much time and trust. Self-doubt and shame can become so pervasive that it colors our self-image as well as the way the person accepts the credibility of others. The inner attitude of the self-ascribed "imposter" goes something like this (either consciously or subconsciously): *If you think I am competent, worthy, and legitimate, then obviously you are either imperceptive, flattering me to make me feel better, or both. Therefore, I must be mistrustful and dismissive of your opinion.*

Many people have distortions in the reality of their thinking. This can range from psychotic delusions to very specific and contained distortions that may be limited to oneself or certain aspects of one's character or performance.

For people with exceedingly high standards (perfectionists among them), assessing their own performance often pits their execution against very high expectations. Whether or not they think they played a good game or accomplished enough will typically omit or discount feedback by or comparison with others. In these cases, they don't feel like imposters, but rather that they've fallen short of expectations, their own and others.

On the other hand, imposters usually remain impervious to reasoning and evidence about the adequacy of their performance and themselves. Their poor self-image and anxiety push back against facts and attempts at persuasion. At some level, coming around to others' perceptions of their value requires a stark realization that they have been fooling themselves for a long time. In itself, this broaches new cause for poor self-confidence and anxiety and can become a vicious cycle of self-doubt, mistrust, and misperceptions.

Living or working with closet imposters can be frustrating and can provoke the feeling of walking on eggshells. Their inner fragility gives rise to oversensitivity, hurt feelings, and the constant need for reassurance. Family and associates may become unwittingly conscripted into their false or constricted reality.

I'm reminded of the anecdote about a man who brought his brother to see a psychiatrist because he (the patient) was convinced he was descended from chickens. After an hour of interviewing and trying unsuccessfully to reason with him, the psychiatrist reported to the brother that treating this disorder would be difficult. With sensitivity, the doctor asked the brother how he could live with such a delusional person.

The brother replied, "Yes, it's difficult, but *we need the eggs.*"

Indeed, illusions, misperceptions, and distorted and perhaps delusional thinking pervade and intrude upon the self-perception and attitude of people who think they are faking it. Treating the anxiety this causes is necessary and fundamental to helping "imposters" become more realistic in their self-assessment and adjust better. But more is required. The credibility of the mentor must be established and augmented. Only when this trust is secure will the self-doubter risk putting aside their tenuous self-perception and be somewhat open to considering alternative facts and presumptions.

Imposter syndrome is one problem that skilled psychotherapy is suited to successfully address. As long as the therapist assumes that recurrent anxiety will not be placated by reassurance alone (and that the anxiety is only mollified through more effective methods), the therapist can turn attention and skills to modifying the patient's views through the edification of *reality testing.*

Reality Testing

Reality testing is a process whereby one's perception of what's so can be tested and validated by consensual agreement. A simple example: If you feel a trembling that seems like an earthquake, you'll be quick to consult some news media or internet source to validate or confirm your experience. You want to see whether it was "just you," and/or gather more information to interpret your experience, predict, and plan.

Another example: if someone behaves rudely or inappropriately, you may be taken aback or even shocked. You may look to others to see what their reaction is and whether they too registered the impropriety.

Many instances abound that require us to use consensual validation or approval to confirm our perceptions and assessments of what's going on around us. Well-integrated people are able to hold personal opinions separate from and in abeyance with their overt reactions to fit the demands of trying situations and people. This requires a brain and self-perception that clearly distinguishes boundaries between self, others, and what each may be thinking or feeling.

Those afflicted with impostor syndrome have trouble navigating such boundaries. Their self-doubt filters into beliefs about transparency and pretense. They often blur those boundaries and cannot distinguish between what they feel and what others can or care to see.

In the process of building reality-testing skills, the mentor poses perceptions and interpretations that serve as alternatives to those expressed by the imposter self. For instance:

"Is it *possible* (maybe not likely, but *possible*) that Mary was not thinking of you negatively?"

"What did she *say or do specifically* that made you feel her disdain?"

Proactive rehearsal is a technique that can help overly self-conscious people better weather their insecurities. I rehearse patients in expressing their anxious anticipations (which I then treat and subdue with Voice Technology). I then give them clues about what to look for in the expressions of other people and how to properly evaluate them. I ask my patients to report back to me their version of what happened, and together we can do a post-assessment and interpretation (with my guidance) of a likely more realistic evaluation of the patient's perceptions and behaviors and the responses of others.

This interactive, before-and-after, repetitive coaching approach has proven to help patients feel less transparent, more legitimate, more appropriate and realistic, and to build attitudes and self-perceptions that are more congruent with reality. Confidence is gradually accrued, such that it is no longer so easily shaken, because it is built upon evidence and probability (unless your ancestors are chickens).

The Divided Self

At some levels, we are all imposters. Seeing ourselves "realistically" is fraught with subjectivity, differing values, and the sensitivities, biases, and doubts of others. To ascertain and nurture an appropriate self-image takes great discipline, humility, and responsiveness to trusted sources (people and God).

Due to personal values, opinions, and defense mechanisms, there is always some disparity and tension between how we see (or would like to see) ourselves, and how others see and appraise us. Disparity need not imply falsehood or being an imposter.

To wend my way through this identity imbroglio, I revert to biblical truths. The book of Romans sheds brilliant light on the divided self, as it reveals the conflict between flesh and spirit, the sin nature and the enlightened nature.

The Bible contains many references to a divided self in human nature since the flesh and spirit are in conflict, spiritually and behaviorally. This is relevant to imposter syndrome in that we strive for virtue, but do things that we do not want to do. Thus, as we fight impulses and accede to higher standards, we vacillate between spiritual aspirations and fleshly desires and actions. Thus, in this struggle we are misrepresenting ourselves in nature and behavior. The "self" I want to be, and sometimes pretend to be, hides the pressure of sin within me. Romans 7 (especially 7:19) captures this cogently.

What shall we say, then? Is the law sinful? Certainly not! Nevertheless,
I would not have known what sin was had it not been for the law. For I

would not have known what coveting really was if the law had not said, "You shall not covet" But sin, seizing the opportunity afforded by the commandment, produced in me every kind of coveting. For apart from the law, sin was dead. Once I was alive apart from the law; but when the commandment came, sin sprang to life and I died. I found that the very commandment that was intended to bring life actually brought death. For sin, seizing the opportunity afforded by the commandment deceived me, and through the commandment put me to death. So then, the law is holy, and the commandment is holy, righteous and good.

Did that which is good, then, become death to me? By no means! Nevertheless, in order that sin might be recognized as sin, it used what is good to bring about my death, so that through the commandment sin might become utterly sinful.

*We know that the law is spiritual; but I am unspiritual, sold as a slave to sin. I do not understand what I do. For what I want to do I do not do, but what I hate I do. And if I do what I do not want to do, I agree that the law is good. As it is, it is no longer I myself who do it, but it is sin living in me. For I know that good itself does not dwell in me, that is, in my sinful nature. For I have the desire to do what is good, but I cannot carry it out. **For I do not do the good I want to do, but the evil I do not want to do—this I keep on doing. Now if I do what I do not want to do, it is no longer I who do it, but it is sin living in me that does it.***

So I find this law at work: Although I want to do good, evil is right there with me. For in my inner being I delight in God's law; but I see another law at work in me, waging war against the law of my mind and making me a prisoner of the law of sin at work within me. What a wretched man I am! Who will rescue me from this body that is subject to death? Thanks be to God, who delivers me through Jesus Christ our Lord!

So then, I myself in my mind am a slave to God's law but in my sinful nature a slave to the law of sin. Romans 7:7–21.

These verses beautifully illustrate the conflict between and within ourselves and the struggle against the hypocrisy that arises from aspiring to spirit and catering to flesh.

Truly, in this regard, we can all be considered imposters. The truth of God's Word exposes the selfish desires and tendencies of the sin nature, while offering hope and resolution of this conflict (See Romans 8) through the spiritual help of Christ.

Coming to Grips With One's Nature

Our human nature forces conflict from inner desires and aspirations, as well as from the demands, complexities, and ambiguities of dealing with others. We must adjudicate and reconcile our own identity views with the needs of others and the evidence of how we operate in the world.

The aphorism, "Fake it until you make it," does not advise being an imposter, but rather advocates persistence and motivation in the quest for achievement, recognition, and confidence.

Within our fallible and corruptible human nature, God has endowed us with an ally to help us navigate through the complexities of anxiety and reality. We are endowed with the compass of a conscience.

CHAPTER 10

Social Anxiety and Phobias

"No man is an island . . ." opens a seventeenth century poem by John Donne. The truth in this metaphor extends throughout our interconnections: social, biological, spiritual, and even existential. We need other people, and others need us. We depend upon people to help us survive and thrive. We have obligations to serve and contribute, to be part of a fabric of family and the community as well. We have social structures and institutions, and we all want to feel that we as individuals matter, and that what we do makes a difference.

Our intricate nervous systems are finely attuned to the sensations, energy, and vibes of other nervous systems. This biological underpinning allows us to selectively draw close to certain individuals, and also may elicit a sense of threat that compels avoidance, retreat, and emotional withdrawal from others.

For many people, anxiety is a great interference, a fearful obstruction to the natural order of satisfying and productive connections and relations with other people. Unfortunately for many, anxiety can become a way of life, a pariah that distorts their sense of safety, ease and comfort, and their communications, and interactions with fellow humans.

Range of Social Anxiety

Discomfort around others encompasses a wide range of sensations, preferences, avoidance, and intensities. Some people are natural loners, preferring solitude, doing things by themselves, or choosing low stimulation over the demands and impingements that flow from human interactions. Self-directed individuals may do things by themselves simply because they like those activities and do not require (or cannot find) others to join them. Preferring (or tolerating) being by oneself does not indicate social anxiety.

With that in mind, there is great diversity in the penchant and tolerance for the company of others. From distrustful or cynical views to severe panic attacks, many people find distress or disappointment in the presence of others. As Mark Twain said, "The more I learn about people, the better I like my dog."

Numerous triggers, thoughts, worries, and circumstances elicit anxiety. Although many people afflicted with chronic anxiety still regularly interact with and relate to fellow humans (and desire to do so), millions of anxious sufferers eschew social interactions and situations that put them in groups of people or circumstances that require conversation with or performance in view of others.

Social anxiety may be characterized by one or more of the following:

Inner self-consciousness, heightened self-focus

Socially anxious individuals have trouble getting their minds off themselves, especially when interacting with or surrounded by others. Super conscious of what others may think of them and how they regard them, they experience a heightened sensitivity that precipitates a cascade of anxious feelings and perceptual distortions (imagining and attributing erroneously what others think about them).

Feelings of exposure or transparency

A socially anxious person feels "under the microscope or spotlight" when expected to speak or when mixing with groups or unfamiliar people. As described in "imposter syndrome," the socially anxious people can sense a disturbing gap between who they perceive themselves to be and the self-image they are trying to project. Interactions feel stressful and fake, and their anxiety centers around fear of exposure—a fear that their inner feelings of pretension, inferiority, and unworthiness will be seen and ridiculed.

Sense of awkwardness

Social anxiety carries a feeling of awkwardness in social situations that may reflect in a person not knowing what to say or how to make conversation that feels genuine, when to speak and listen, and what to do with one's body when in the presence of others.

Feeling isolated, out of step

The awkwardness sensed (and sometimes expressed) by the anxious person makes them feel isolated and out of step regarding appropriate behaviors and interactions that will be accepted and welcomed.

Fear or projection of being judged negatively

Part and parcel of social anxiety is the fear and expectation of being judged negatively, looked down upon, and rejected. This occurs in the mindset of anxiety without any external objective evidence that this is thought or expressed by others. The heightened self-consciousness can make a person exaggerate awkward moments or overreact to comments by others.

Insufficient social skills

While the socially anxious person projects or attributes perceptions and judgments by others without reference to or verified evidence of them, it may also be true that the anxious person may indeed lack polished or even appropriate social skills. If these deficits exist, they are only reinforced by fear and lack of social engagement that correlates with social anxiety, becoming a negatively spiraling loop.

Low self-confidence

Social anxiety is further magnified by low self-confidence. In turn, the lack of confidence inhibits social interaction and practice, thereby contributing to a cycle that sustains low self-confidence.

Physiological symptoms

Anxiety often triggers physiological symptoms such as fight-or-flight responses including increased heart rate, sweating, chest tightness and difficulty breathing, racing thoughts, flushing, and a host of other body discomforts. The anxious individual becomes mortified and embarrassed, fearing that others will notice these reactions. Such responses can then induce a panic reaction that seeks escape from the triggering situation.

Compromised reality testing

Reality testing refers to one's ability to perceive, interpret, and make accurate judgments about events; the perceptions, intents, and motivations of others; as well as one's own effect upon others based on actual evidence—responses from others, consequences, feedback, and consensual agreement—the common perceptions and interpretations that most people have in a given situation.

This stands in contrast to idiosyncratic, overly personalized, distorted, or confabulated ideas and perceptions that a person may have that are not shared or validated by others. At an extreme, people with delusions or hallucinations have markedly impaired reality testing. They cannot easily distinguish between fact and their own fiction or fantasies. At subtler levels, socially anxious people are so overwhelmed by their intrusive thoughts and feelings that they project that others feel as they do, thinking they see through others, making negative and disparaging judgments, though not necessarily expressed.

Avoidance As a Lifestyle

Feeling discomfort in social situations spurs many with this type of anxiety to avoid social contact. This may be especially acute regarding even small groups of people (even two or three) or new or unfamiliar situations. Some severely afflicted individuals can barely leave their home. This condition in the extreme is known as agoraphobia.

A large contingent of socially anxious (withdrawn, uncomfortable, immature, or unskilled) individuals develop a restricted lifestyle, which is increasingly possible with the glut of media distractions (cellphone, TV, online videos, music, and games). The attraction of media and technology that does not involve social interaction makes it easy and comfortable to entertain oneself, withdraw, and hide from the stimulation and demands that human interaction requires.

When my children were growing up (prior to Facebook), they claimed to have many "friends" online. I reminded them that, although one can have online friends and maintain healthy relationships long distance, we are still mammals and, as such, true friendships require *some* physical proximity. (Thankfully, my children became very social and integrated, despite their gaming and internet devotion.)

I remember a patient from decades ago—an attractive and bright thirteen-year-old girl—who answered my question about whether she has friends, "Yes, my phone."

Social Relations in the Digital Era

The effects and ramifications of digital and social media are revealing many significant downsides. The extent to which these technologies blunt or impair skills and development in relationships remains under scrutiny and is a growing concern. The "scrolling" lifestyle has induced much harm, stunted development, and unleashed aggressive and mean behavior, promulgated by clandestine clicks and attempts to cloak one's identity.

Even for the socially "sensitive," digital media invites appeal and temptation to seek and solicit anonymous admiration and approval. Predators, exhibitionists, racists, lurkers, and others seem emboldened to hide behind their devices and avoid the consequences and "appropriate" anxiety of navigating acceptable interactional dynamics.

A preponderance of fearful and insecure folks substitute digital endeavors for true and meaningful human interaction. Some may recognize their fear, while others delude themselves about the viability and integrity of digital relationships.

This era of online dating is increasingly risky as scammers proliferate. The skills, ambiguity, and roles needed for meeting and "courting" have receded behind the habit of *swiping*.

Treating and Mitigating Social Anxiety

Among the various anxiety disorders, social anxiety tends to be more complex and difficult to treat. Fortunately, social anxiety can be treated quite effectively with a combination of TFT, neurofeedback, and targeted mentoring.

Therapists are known for giving "good" advice—but cannot control the obstacles in patient implementation and follow-through. This is notoriously true for social anxiety and procrastination. The very nature of the disorder prohibits people from moving forward effectively. Their anxiety is stultifying and overwhelming. However, this is where TFT and neurofeedback make breakthroughs. Once the paralyzing anxiety is diminished and held at bay, a person has a reasonable opportunity to take risks and try less familiar or comfortable behavior.

Therapists experienced in TFT and neurofeedback usually have a greater advantage when adding their other therapeutic skills productively to the mix. In the mentoring process (or coaching or counseling), the therapist assists the patient in rehearsing scenarios of social engagement, drawing out fears, projected imagination, and then planning and practicing responses. This is quite different from cognitive behavior therapy in that the objective and practice is not to form different thoughts to mitigate the anxiety, but rather to *validate* the expectation, *rehearse and implement* strategies, and subsequently to *enlist* the therapist's guidance in evaluating the results of a patient's behaviors and experiences with social encounters.

This "post-mortem" process is invaluable in helping socially anxious people to properly evaluate how they did in subjective feelings as well as in evidentiary behavior. Although the therapist is not *there* in the actual situation, by carefully interviewing and questioning the patient within a trusted therapeutic alliance, the mentor can evoke enough information to guide the patient in determining appropriate and realistic judgments about their role and how they came across in the social event.

This process relies on building reality testing skills to shape and buttress more accurate and helpful interpretations (including the assessment of maladaptive behavior and faulty perceptions) for more objective evaluation and for future planning.

To move through this process requires a calm nervous system. The socially anxious person needs encouragement and assistance to alter the conditioned inertia that inhibits most initiative and risk-taking.

In the process of building reality testing skills, the mentor can pose perceptions and interpretations that serve as alternatives to those expressed by the scared self. For instance: "Is it *possible* (maybe not likely, but *possible*) that John was not thinking of you negatively?" Or "What did he *say or do specifically* that made you feel his disdain?"

Proactive rehearsal can help overly self-conscious people better weather their insecurities. I rehearse patients in expressing their anxious anticipations (which is then treated and subdued with Voice Technology). I provide useful clues about what to look for in the expressions of other people and how to properly evaluate them. I ask my patients to report back to me their version of what happened, and together we can do a guided post-assessment and interpretation of a likely more realistic evaluation of the patient's perceptions and behaviors and the responses of others.

This interactive, before-and-after, repetitive coaching approach helps patients feel safer, less transparent, more legitimate, more appropriate and realistic, and more able to build attitudes and self-perceptions that are more congruent with reality. Confidence is gradually accrued, such that it is no longer so easily shaken, because it is built upon evidence and probability, gradually accumulated and validated through real-life interactions.

When fears are eliminated, negative fantasies quell in the light of exposure, and anxiety is substantially reduced, making patients more amenable to learning and practicing social skills that may be absent or underdeveloped.

For instance, many people do not know how to make good conversation (effectively communicate verbally). Though painfully aware of this and perhaps magnifying their self-consciousness, a person may have an actual deficiency that sustains this anxiety. Part of the solution is to build and repair this aspect of social etiquette. Teaching a person how to ask questions that elicit comfortable conversation, how to actively listen, and how to subtly draw out another person are invaluable aids to making interactions smoother. Socially anxious people typically are so self-focused that they have poor timing, causing them to misinterpret cues and opportunities for acknowledging communications, or reflect on what is said, negotiate moments for disclosure, and recognize or solicit feedback from their "audience."

Conversation is a responsibility that should also be enjoyable and comfortably stimulating. The ability to engage in conversation is well recognized as an art and skill that often requires coaching, modeling, and practice. The socially anxious person may need to catch up or brush up on these skills along with reducing the anxiety that inhibits them.

Eyes On the Prize

With respectful acknowledgment and consideration of those afflicted with social anxiety, we all need to get our minds off ourselves and focus more on other people—not critically—but *observationally*, divesting ourselves as much as we can of using others to service our egos.

The saying, "It's not about you" serves us well, and we would all do well to make a greater focus on others a lifestyle and relational habit. This is particularly useful as a guideline for the socially anxious, who tend to be so self-absorbed with inner terror that their focus on others is distorted or compromised.

In striving to attain most goals, we encounter obstacles, adversity, and frustration, needing to mine grit and perseverance, while deferring negative intrusions and keeping our eyes on the prize. Winners develop this habit. Such a focus is necessary relational nutrition for the ego-starved and socially anxious.

Remember that most people are chronically thinking about themselves. When we get out of our own heads and focus on others, more favorable outcomes will result.

Phobias

A phobia is an irrational fear that persists despite little or no actual threat. Millions of people suffer from phobias. Those who struggle with phobias actually *know* their fears may be *irrational*, but they remain powerless to face or dismantle them. Cognitive tools and tricks are largely ineffective for eliminating phobias for the sound reason that these fears are not rational—they don't respond to logic, will, or re-framing of the problem. Statistics on the miniscule probability of plane crashes do nothing to mitigate the fear of flying. Indeed, offering such "help" often makes the phobic person feel even worse.

Similarly, people who imagine and fear more abstract, potential events—such as becoming ill, a family member suffering harm, or even vague premonitions about the danger of venturing away from home—are not reassured or calmed by explanations and probabilities. This is the nature of such irrational fears.

Fortunately, phobias respond extremely well to TFT. In a matter of minutes, phobias can be eliminated, regardless of their intensity or historical longevity. Thousands of times, I have completely eliminated strangulating phobias in one or two sessions with Voice Technology (and this can also be done, though less quickly, using diagnostic TFT).

Phobias have evolutionary roots. Common fears (darkness, snakes, the unknown) are wired into our makeup to protect us from a very threatening world. Somehow, certain evolutionary patterns have mor-phed into the genetic potential of certain individuals, such that these irrational fears germinate and persist. The recalcitrant fear is caused by a fusion of thoughts and feelings encapsulated in a negative thought field with disruptive uneasiness.

The Solutions section explains how TFT separates the thought or provoking stimulus from the agitated feeling, like tapping in a code that instantaneously turns off the alarm in the body. The success rate for eliminating phobias in general is remarkably and reliably high. Though fears can reactivate (usually due to toxins), they are easily again eliminated, and the offending toxins that prompted their return can be identified and avoided.

Phobias occur in two types: simple and complex. Simple phobias react to specific stimuli, such as flying, driving on bridges or highways, snakes, bugs, etc., which are easily treated and eliminated with TFT. Complex phobias are more generalized, but are also quite amenable to elimination. Health fears and social anxiety fall into this category. These fears often have multiple and layered thought fields that take more time and strategy to uncover and treat effectively. Neurofeedback is also quite helpful in treating phobias, although it takes more time. I have found that people who suffer from chronic and pervasive anxiety—which may include different phobias—do best with a combination of TFT and neurofeedback.

Social anxiety consists of multiple levels of neurological and psychological disturbances that intertwine and develop into pervasive anxiety centered around fear and discomfort with people in social or less-familiar situations. As with other forms of anxiety, this complex and debilitating condition responds well to TFT and neurofeedback, partnered with targeted mentoring, including reality testing, rehearsal and evaluation, and social skills training. Neurofeedback is also instrumental in activating the hemispheric functions that develop these nonverbal perceptions and skills that socially awkward or anxious people are typically not keen at sensing, such as nonverbal cues in body language, facial expressions, speech cadence, and intonations.

A Treatment Plan for Healing Social Anxiety

Here is an outline describing essential components of a practical plan to address social anxiety, combining technologies to get rid of anxiety with socially relevant aspects that contribute to better interactions and improved confidence.

Eliminate anxiety, worry, fears, and traumas.

As described throughout *Overcome Anxiety*, I endorse the use of EEG neurofeedback and Voice Technology to eliminate anxiety. Voice Technology works immediately and is used to purge the "perturbations" or codes that keep negative emotions (including anxiety, fear, trauma, etc.) held in place. EEG neurofeedback trains the brain and nervous system to remain calm and self-regulated, especially in response to internal distress and environmental provocation. When anxiety is eliminated, flexibility to consider options, think and plan rationally, and perceive more objectively all become more available, and positive behavior change comes more easily.

Address key aftereffects of anxiety: obsessiveness and procrastination.

The socially anxious person typically obsesses over fears and fantasies about discomfort in the presence of others and tends to avoid and procrastinate obligations and opportunities that require social contact. A combination of Voice Technology and behavioral planning and contracting can overcome these impediments. Adding reality testing, rehearsal and evaluation, and evaluative feedback solidifies and advances confidence and containment of interfering thoughts.

Plan social interactions and communications, including goals, expectations, and contingencies.

Because those with social anxiety avoid contact and withdraw from social interactions, they may have vague or unrealistic expectations and plans regarding social engagement. They need assistance in setting incremental goals and confidence-building steps to interact with others. This is the type of assistance that experienced mentors and therapists can provide.

Make a contract.

Commitment is key to changing behavior. Because the socially anxious person has "hit the wall" so often with overwhelming anxiety, the prospects for follow-through have dimmed. Consequently, the expectations for success and confidence have concurrently diminished. When inner anxiety is at bay, it's possible to make a plan, commit, and execute the plan. Only then can realistic appraisals and adjustments be made.

Consistently report on follow-through events and emotional experiences.

Consistent communication with the mentor/therapist is vital for support, as well as assessment and interpretation of the patient's experiences and perceptions. As the patient begins to explore and experiment with (or revisit) social interactions, emotional responses and control can be monitored and tempered.

Engage in interactive evaluation and reality testing.

Before and after social interactions, the anxious person and a therapist can engage in the processes of anticipating what the social interactions might be like (possible scenarios and expected feelings), how the interactions proceed, and how the patient feels and thinks about what happened. This allows the person to express concerns and feedback in a safe environment and to receive therapist feedback to help interpret the experiences more realistically and without projection or drama.

For example, based on what the person reports, the therapist can highlight and reinforce the adaptive behaviors (e.g., "You took a chance, despite your apprehensions" . . . "You got through it without a panic attack" . . . "So-and-so told you it was good to see you") and can challenge the patient's negative assessments of the event and his performance (e.g., "Where is the evidence that people saw your anxiety or bad-mouthed you? Did anyone say anything to you to make that credible?").

Challenge perceptual distortions and the reality bases for negative self-perceptions and self-denigration with a clinician.

Socially anxious people habitually internalize (and may express) negative feelings and perceptions about their behaviors and the responses of others. They do this partly out of the need for reassurance, but also resulting from projections of their imagination that feed and reinforce their own negative and weak self-image.

For example, a patient may report that people looked down on them, that it was hard to make conversation and the conversation was phony or shallow, and/or that others could sense their anxiety. This creates the opportunity for the therapist to challenge these (probably erroneous) perceptions and conclusions by asking the patient to provide concrete evidence to support these interpretations and associated feelings. By systematically eliminating anxiety, and subsequently challenging the habitual negative interpretations of social events and performances, the therapist and patient can build new and more realistic constructions of how the person acted and how such actions came across to others. This is known as *covert assessment and reality testing.*

Construct step-wise shaping behavior modification schedules for social behaviors.

Using the "inch-by-inch, life's a cinch; yard-by-yard, life is hard" model, a therapist can help a socially uncomfortable patient make small, incremental inroads toward increasing social overtures and experiences, and develop new and more flexible repertoires that build competence and confidence.

The therapist can suggest and encourage social behaviors including get-togethers, phone and electronic communications, and healthier skills and habits to brainstorm, initiate, and respond to social opportunities.

Build social skills where necessary.

It's often (but not universally) the case that socially anxious people have awkward or underdeveloped interactional skills. Though their emotional responses are exaggerated and also underpinned by traumas, the reality bases of their social experiences may indeed incorporate inadequate social behaviors on their part. Therefore, in some cases, teaching social skills supports and refines the process of building social comfort and productive participation.

Some components of building social skills:

1. Verbal bids and invitations. Teach role play how to initiate social contacts: make overtures and invitations, use appropriate language, stay upbeat and positive, ask questions and listening actively.

2. Body language. Monitor postures, facial expressions, and eliminate defensiveness.

3. Validation checks. Clarify communications and intentions (e.g., "I'm not sure if you're saying you can't make it next Tuesday or you're just declining my invitation in general. I'll accept what you say, but I want to get your message the way you mean it.")

4. Feedback and boundaries. Teach and rehearse to become communicative and assertive in the face of someone else behaving inappropriately or overstepping boundaries.

Build confidence through practice, cumulative experience, and success.

Social ease requires that anxiety be subdued. This begins with the brain and nervous system. Then success generates to the real world, expanding outward and achieving modest and increasing successes. Anxiety is first eliminated *in vitro* (when *thinking* about past or impending scenarios). But the acid test is when the person engages without anxiety (or medication) *in vivo* (in the actual situation), thereupon building and reinforcing actual reality-based, real-time success in overcoming the problem. Repetition of success builds habit and confidence.

People who have been withdrawn and ruminated for years must be healed and gradually introduced, taught, and reinforced for real-world successes.

It can be done!

PART II

SOLUTIONS: GET POSITIVE RESULTS

I was stumbling through life, like playing soccer wearing flip-flops. Your treatment gave me shoes, and now I am surefooted!

—a patient I treated with TFT and EEG neurofeedback

CHAPTER 11

Eliminate Anxiety Rapidly: Thought Field Therapy

I fully endorse a revolutionary technique for rapidly eliminating any negative emotion in minutes. This technique, called Thought Field Therapy (TFT), is extremely effective in relieving all forms of anxiety and related distress. TFT does not require any equipment, and a therapist is not needed to carry out many parts of TFT treatment. TFT can be self-administered with quick and effective results. However some people may not respond as well to self-treatment. I will share the basics of TFT self-treatment and the reasons TFT works so well.

Although negative emotions are a part of our makeup, all too often they drive our behavior and attitudes, even without our realizing how pivotal they are in promoting or interfering with our capacity to live intact. Rampant negative emotions can disable or paralyze the psychological flexibility we require to engage alternate responses, colluding with our mind's negative and justifying narrative and keeping us stuck.

What Is Thought Field Therapy?

Thought Field Therapy (TFT) is a powerful yet simple treatment for dealing with psychological disturbances by manipulating how energy flows in the body. When applied to a psychological problem an individual is experiencing, TFT provides a code that eliminates "perturbations" in the thought field that are the fundamental cause of all negative emotions—the process is similar to reprogramming a computer task by revising computer codes. A disturbance in the encoding of information that connects a thought with a feeling is called a perturbation. By finger tapping on specific energy points in a particular sequence, the TFT process causes these perturbations to collapse, and renders them inactive.

TFT was developed by Dr. Roger Callahan,[10] who began this work in the 1970s and continued to expand and refine the methods and applications. He published seminal works about TFT and trained thousands of professionals in its therapeutic utilization. In my experience working with and learning from Dr. Callahan, I saw firsthand how effective this method is, and I have used it now for decades on my own patients.

At its inception, TFT was used primarily to eliminate anxiety-based problems such as phobias and panic, as well as various types of trauma. Over the years, practitioners have expanded the range of applications and now effectively use TFT to assist in the treatment of many ailments, including physical ills such as headaches, digestive upsets, and body pain. Startling developments in the practical applications of TFT have included its use in Kosovo and Africa to treat war trauma and many variants of the posttraumatic stress and injury associated with violence, loss, abandonment, torture, and deprivation.

TFT has wide-ranging applications for the relief of all types of negative emotions, as well as symptoms of physiological distress and psychological self-sabotage. The technique works fast with remarkable efficacy. And self-help versions of TFT are easy to use, convenient, and contribute to self-control and self-empowerment.

To begin to fathom how and why TFT works, we must remember

10. See https://www.goodtherapy.org/learn-about-therapy/types/thought-field-therapy

that nature uses various codes to operate, signal, and modify the world. Humans use codes, consciously and biologically, in many ways.

Thought Field Therapy (TFT) Terms

Thought Field Therapy: A treatment for psychological disturbances that provides a *code* that, when applied to a psychological problem on which the individual is focusing, will eliminate *perturbations* in the thought field, the fundamental cause of all negative emotions.

Thought Field: A *field* is an invisible, nonmaterial structure in space that has an effect upon matter. A *thought field* is a connection between cognitive awareness and emotions that generates a field that may contain perturbations.

Perturbation: The fundamental cause of all negative emotions, perturbations are the physiological, neurological, hormonal, chemical, and cognitive events that result in the experience of specific negative emotions.

Cure: The elimination of all subjective experience of distress and symptoms associated with a problem.[11] In TFT, a cure is brought about by eliminating perturbations in the thought field.

Nature's Codes

Nature overflows with secrets and mysteries contained in codes. From DNA to language, symbols, and relationships, the world is embedded with information about how life unfolds. Managing life requires the detection, translation, and enactment of the codes that encapsulate this information. We use codes for analyzing and synthesizing data, formulating concepts and logic, testing hypotheses, evaluating options, and generalizing from our individual and collective experiences the characteristics, resources, and courses of action that help us survive and live better.

---

11. In psychological treatment and research, a measure of subjective distress that is often used is a rating scale called a SUD (subjective unit of distress), whereby a person rates their distress on a scale of 1–10, where 10 is the most distress conceivable and 1 represents no distress or symptom.

Codes sum up the rules and messages about these processes. For example, when driving, we respond to traffic lights at an intersection. We use social codes to indicate our receptivity and availability, and we react to the green/red light messages that tell whether it is okay to proceed on a course. We are attuned to people's facial expressions that convey whether to advance, back off, or wait. Codes communicate when the airplane bathroom is vacant, the degree to which a social gesture is welcome, when a boundary has been violated, and even when a partner might be interested in sex. Formally or informally taught cognitive codes that are reflected in expressive language, grammatical conventions, spelling rules, mathematics, and economic principles allow us to communicate our ideas and exchange goods and services.

Nature imparts information by means of environmental and biological codes. Examples include barometric pressure that indicates when it is likely to rain, cramping or bloating that indicate when a menstrual period is coming, and fatigue and stress that signal the need to rest, retreat, and recover.

Codes for Identification, Communication, and Brain Function

Codes embed information and are akin to shorthand. They are shortcut methods for abbreviating, storing, and communicating information. In a sense, they are like our Social Security number and the many PIN codes and passwords we create that identify us and we use to access private information. For example, when you click on a computer link, you may be asked to enter a code before entry is granted. Though we may not be consciously aware of it, information we hear or see is also in code.

The English language contains twenty-six letters that can be combined to form words, sentences, and limitless ideas. When we read or listen to information, we're decoding the words in accordance with accepted rules of phonetics, pronunciation, and grammar. If we understand what the decoded words mean, we can process and assimilate the encoded information. If the information is represented in numbers (e.g., the balance of our checking account) and we've mastered the meaning of these number codes, we are then able to respond accordingly.

Biological data can be decoded, and by breaking the codes, beneficial alterations in human response patterns can be achieved. We can essentially replace harmful or distressing codes with those that are beneficial and healing. TFT allows such "replacements" to occur. For many people, this is a radical concept to consider: that the body and mind store coded information that keeps emotional and physical problems in place, and that by decoding and reprogramming this information, negative feelings and problems can be alleviated within minutes.

Think of the function of the codes that our body stores as a kind of emotional alarm system. The alarm is set within us by reactions we have to traumas, upsets, and even to foods and medicines. TFT works by deactivating the internal alarm and by offsetting the signals that trigger the alarms. We accomplish this by tapping with our fingers on specific points on our body in a specific order. The tapping sends energy signals throughout our nervous system via meridian points and pathways. These signals disrupt the *perturbations* that are causing the distress, and they essentially reset our system back to normal for the particular problem that was upsetting us.

To grasp the concept of how pressing with our finger can create so much impact, think of a garage door opener. Or better yet, think of how tapping several numbers into a phone can send specific messages over a great distance with great speed and impact.

Once the negative emotional charge is removed, we can think clearly about the problem, but it will no longer bother us at all. *Poof!*

An interesting and common phenomenon that often occurs after a rapid TFT treatment that totally eliminates the problem, is when the treated person says, "I can't think about it anymore." What the person really means is: *When I think about it, it doesn't bother me, so why think about it?*

In general, tapping on meridian points can have a beneficial effect. Indeed, there are several "look-alike" tapping treatments that claim efficacy, and some work to a certain degree. However, the detection of the disruptive codes and application of the functional codes are the real secrets to TFT's astounding and consistent success.

These curative codes are elicited through TFT's causal diagnostic procedure that permitted the development of the TFT algorithms. The algorithms are shortcuts or general tapping recipes that have emerged over time as common tapping sequences. They can be self-administered while thinking of the problem, and they are often effective in eliminating the problem. An algorithm treatment is presented here to help you get started in eliminating your own negative emotions.

The fundamental cause of emotional distress, including anxiety and cravings, is the phenomenon of perturbation in the thought field. This specific type of information that resides in the thought field contains the instructions for triggering and thus generating the chemical and neurological events that lead to what we call negative or disturbing emotions. Many of these perturbations are inherited, and some are established during the lifetime of the individual. Regardless of the origin, TFT makes it possible to eliminate these negative emotions at their fundamental source.

Chemical events in the human body will ultimately result in negative emotions as well as associated cognitive thoughts and related neurological activity. The basic premise of TFT, however, is that the perturbations in the thought field precede and generate these chemical and cognitive events. Perturbations in the thought field form the fundamental and basic cause of all disturbed or negative emotions, and are subsumed and rendered inoperative with successful TFT treatment. The successful therapeutic treatment of the perturbation eliminates the chemical and cognitive consequences. (The perturbation is the basic causal factor and the chemistry and cognition are considered secondary and tertiary.)

Proof of this phenomenon exists at physiological *and* psychological levels. At the physiological level, research shows that *heart rate variability* (HRV) improves dramatically after TFT treatment.[12] Because of this, I especially recommend TFT treatment to anyone with a history of heart problems.

At the psychological level, a person's narrative changes dramatically after treatment. Because patients in distress routinely feel impelled to repeat their description of symptoms and all the negative

---

12. Heart rate variability (HRV) is a primary indicator of the body's resources to survive and adapt to internal and external challenges. Poor HRV is associated with morbidity and premorbid disease conditions. HRV is one of the most researched variables in medicine. Until recently, scientists did not have methods of improving HRV significantly and rapidly. My colleagues and I have shown dramatic improvements in HRV after a single TFT session (Pignotti and Steinberg, 2001).

ramifications, I ask my patients to do the TFT treatment first, and I promise to listen to their story for as long as they want afterward. Almost always after a TFT treatment of just a few minutes, the patient has no story to tell—the symptoms that were driving the story (which seemed very real and rooted in external circumstances) have essentially *disappeared*.

TFT vs. Programming

Using TFT to eliminate distress is different from other approaches. Conventional methods and beliefs rely upon assumptions that neurochemical imbalances must be targeted directly, usually through medication, and/or cognitive patterns of thinking and beliefs must be modified in order get rid of negative emotions, unpleasant mood states, intrusive thinking, and their associated dysfunctional behaviors. TFT unabashedly challenges and disproves these assumptions by virtue of its tangible and consistent success.

You can probably imagine the consternation and dismissive attitude on the part of those who believe that this seemingly silly and innocuous treatment could not possibly work. Yet despite such skepticism, TFT is scientifically based, highly researched, and replicated, and continues to gain adherents who benefit from its simple, natural, and effective methods.

When we are seeking to relieve distress and change negative patterns, it is reasonable to postulate theories and question traditional assumptions (based on lack of evidence) that particular early life experiences or tendencies produce specific or predictable outcomes later in life. The traditional theories of psychological development that link behavior patterns to early programming fail to acknowledge the many exceptions, and the huge variability in how people turn out despite earlier life disadvantages. Most importantly, reliance upon these assumptions about environmental influences provides no *reliable* therapeutic path to avoid character defects or the psychological damage that results from early experiences—nor a *reliable* therapeutic roadmap for repairing the related defects or damage. The traditional contention that early character formation and development are immutable suggests a sad determinism that overshadows free will, intention, purpose, fortitude, miracles, and divine intervention.

In place of this self-fulfilling cycle of determinism and victimization, I have written about the *phenomenon of challenge,* denoting the undergirding reality that can turn trials and tribulations into opportunities and successes. A primary practical way to use a challenge to our advantage is to apply it to controlling and eliminating negative emotions. We must learn to differentiate the negative emotions that intermittently bring about anguish and distress from the unique, enduring, and constructive qualities (including some negative emotions) that positively form our character, our sense of self, and the ways in which we interact with others. This distinction is vital in eliminating disturbing and incapacitating symptoms quickly.

To feel better, we don't all need to spend years in therapy remodeling our personality. I have worked with thousands of people who had been previously (and unsuccessfully) treated that way. These people remained troubled after traditional treatment, and their failure to be cured reflected the fundamental paradox inherent in the traditional talk-therapy therapeutic model and also in the belief systems of most people experiencing emotional distress. Traditional therapy (and its influences on popular beliefs about the "requirements" for getting better) is predicated on the concept that those in treatment can find relief from negative symptoms only through an understanding and analysis of deep-seated conflicts, motivations, habits, and early traumas. With this model, clients are conditioned to accept a long course of introspection, treatment, and character development, and an extensive analysis of the psychological determinants of behavior. Clients may achieve personal insights, and sometimes believe they are getting better, but they are not cured.

The central irony is that the very benefits that appropriate psychotherapy can achieve are often blocked by the negative emotional states that prompt the therapy in the first place. When a person is thinking clearly and not dependent upon the therapist to soothe his disruptive moods, psychotherapy can be useful for issues such as exploring one's identity and values, challenging belief systems, reality constructs and perceptual distortions, developing better communication skills, and practicing life skills. But a person may enter therapy to change dysfunctional relationship patterns in which the person is hurtful or abusive and is, ironically, often unable to appreciate or implement psychological advice or insights because of uncontrollable feelings (anger, rage, rejection, jealousy, etc.).

Eliminating negative emotional control is a *prerequisite* to effective psychological change, not a result of it. Confusion over this principle has kept too many people suffering and powerless for way too long. Fortunately, the extraordinary healing of TFT can change this fast. When negative emotions subside, exceptional learning, progress, and positive behavior change can occur. Once freed from the pressure of fear and anxiety, people are much more receptive to guidance, feedback, new opportunities, and growth. With this highly focused and effective intervention, negative emotional problems, such as anxiety, depression, anger, compulsions, cravings, stress, loneliness, and trauma, can actually be eliminated in minutes!

That Fast?

One might ask, "How can this possibly happen within minutes?"

Good question!

To answer this question, let's review some realities we usually take for granted, and compare their relevance to feeling well. Take body temperature, for example. We are warm-blooded animals who must maintain body temperature within a relatively narrow range in order to function. When body temperature fluctuates more than a few degrees, we become not only symptomatic (chills, fever), we also become at risk for survival. Fortunately, the human body has built-in mechanisms for maintaining and regulating body temperature, as it does for many other functions, including emotional "temperature."

When body temperature is controlled, it is difficult to feel or even imagine a physical threat from heat or cold. However, step outside in subzero temperatures or sit in a bath that is too hot, and you will know firsthand the experience of responding rapidly to environmental changes with negative feelings. However, the reverse—experiencing rapid changes in positive feelings—is also possible, and yet taken for granted!

Physical examples that illustrate this principle also provide relevance to emotional healing. When you come in from the cold or remove the source of the heat, your body quickly acclimates back to its accustomed range of comfortable operation. Unless you were exposed to the point of actual physical injury (burns, frostbite, or hypothermia), you recover relatively quickly, usually within minutes. Given the degree of threat posed by "the elements," this rapid recovery might seem surprising—yet we take it for granted since temperature acclimatization is within our experience and happens automatically and consistently.

Physical illness also illustrates the self-healing/self-regulating phenomenon. When stricken by viruses such as the "twenty-four-hour flu," we have experienced the massive discomfort that accompanies a high fever as our bodily defenses mobilize to contain the offending microbes. Although such illness takes longer than a few minutes to dissipate, the critical period when the fever "breaks" is followed by a rapid acceleration in recovery, and a noticeable relief or "feeling better." This process occurs naturally, with or without medication, independent of the sufferer's beliefs or understandings about what is happening.

We take for granted that the process of returning to normalcy will happen relatively quickly. With rare exceptions, people don't live with high fevers for very long. The body's immune system must overcome and contain the invading pathogens. Our white blood cells surround foreign organisms to encapsulate them and prevent them from multiplying and taking over our bodies. This isolation of the pathogens usually happens automatically (although we can take steps to facilitate the process), regardless of whether or not we intellectually comprehend the ever-vigilant, self-healing phenomenon operating within our body.

In a similar manner, nature has encoded mechanisms within us to absorb, fight, and mitigate emotional and psychological invasions. To ensure survival, nature insists that we subdue threat, lest it overpower and defeat us. The psychologically programmed mechanism that reduces emotional threats isolates them by tucking them away (encoding them) into specific energy and nervous system disruptions that are much less of a threat to the entire organism. These isolated and specific disruptions (perturbations) are activated by thought fields—the emotional discomfort that is aroused when a person thinks about something connected to the original perturbation. Thoughts connected with the "encoded" threat are what is experienced as the symptoms of a psychological problem. TFT is an ideally suited and simple tool for treating those symptoms—effectively reprogramming the mechanism to override the perturbations.

How TFT Works in Practice

The application of TFT is done by a process of finger tapping on meridian points on the upper body when experiencing the negative emotion or urge you want to eliminate. The tapping can be done with either hand and on either side of the body. Self-tapping is preferable, as this is more convenient, allows for greater autonomy and self-sufficiency, and diminishes potential problems that may arise from "touching" patients. But another person may also administer tapping if that is easier or needed for any reason.

Regardless of who administers the tapping, the effectiveness is derived from energy put into the body by the tapping. The same meridian points used in acupuncture are also receptors to noninvasive pressure such as tapping. When applied at the appropriate junctures in the correct sequences, the tapping *transduces* (converts and sends) the slight physical/kinesthetic energy into signals to the brain and nervous system, which changes information and reprograms the linkages between thoughts and feelings. This allows people to eliminate negative emotions and empowers them to change behavior.

This concept is easy to recognize in its application to many other operations we take for granted. For example, garage door openers work on the same principle: a slight touch on a remote sends a signal that transduces radio waves into mechanical energy, causing a physical change that is disproportionate to the energy applied. The programming of an alarm is similar, where tapping in the appropriate code will disengage the alarm.

This is how TFT works. And this is why TFT is so powerful and consistent in the elimination of negative emotions such as anxiety and addictive urges. TFT uses our body's natural wisdom to store, manipulate, and unlock codes that affect our conscious and subconscious thoughts, feelings, and behavioral motivations. The locations and sequences of tapping points are determined by codes; and the process of decoding the disturbance (caused by perturbations) comprises the diagnostic aspects of TFT. Certain eye movements as well as humming may be used at some points in the process.

When the mind and body are in distress, the thought field is connected to a negative emotional state by a code, and the appropriate tapping breaks the connection with the embedded code that set created the disturbance in the first place.

Step-by-Step Instruction for Eliminating Negative Emotions (Self-Help through Algorithms)

TFT can be used to treat any negative emotion. For the purpose of introduction and instruction, let's use anxiety and cravings (or addictive urges) as the negative emotion you want to eliminate. Cravings and addictive urges span a spectrum of severity and frequency, but most of us have urges and cravings we prefer not to have. Anxiety is the cause of these urges, and anxiety is a fundamental negative emotion that drives much of uncomfortable narratives and problematic behaviors.

To locate the tapping points, refer to the diagram. Generally, tap each point fifteen times (except for the gamut spot, as described below).

Review all the steps to get a sense of the process but, for the first treatment, try to wait until your anxiety or urge is quite high in order to experience the dramatic power of the treatment. After that, repeat the treatments any time you are aware of any anxiety or unwanted urge or craving at all.

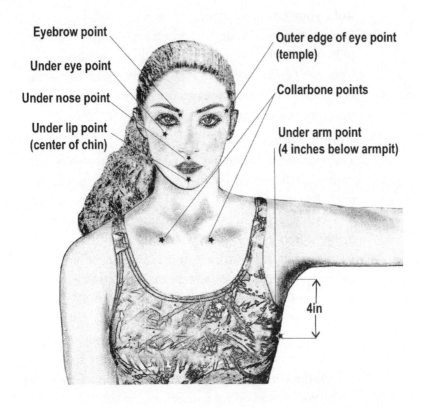

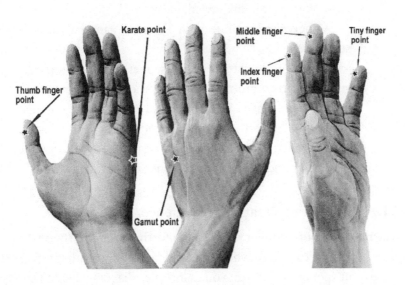

1. **Rate your anxiety/urge.**

   Rate the degree of your urge on a ten-point scale in order to best guide the treatments. Write down the number from one (no anxiety/urge at all) to ten (the anxiety/urge is highest) that best expresses the degree of the urge at the current moment.

2. **Treat the urge.**

   Throughout the treatment, consider how easy it would be to indulge that particular feeling of anxiety or addictive urge. Take the first two fingers of either hand and tap underneath one of your eyes (See diagram). Tap solidly and firmly 15X, but do not hurt yourself.

   Then tap the collarbone point (15X); next tap the underarm point that is located four inches below your armpit (15X), and then the collarbone point again (15X).

   If your anxiety/urge remains the same after these treatments, a useful corrective procedure called psychological reversal is summarized after the next step. Once you do the corrective procedure, and tap under your eyes again, you should notice a definite (not subtle) and clear reduction in your anxiety/addictive urge.

   Otherwise continue with the nine-gamut treatment sequence

   When the anxiety or urge disappears, some people assume that they are not following the instructions, since they are no longer thinking about or focusing on their problem. This is the natural phenomenon of the logical mind (or left-brain interpreter) trying to rationalize the new experience—the disappearance of the anxiety/urge.

The Nine-Gamut Treatment Sequence

The nine-gamut treatment will result in further reducing the anxiety or urge. Continue to think of your urge, and tap solidly (with two fingers) the gamut spot on the back of your hand (See diagram) behind and between the little finger knuckle and the ring finger knuckle on the back of your hand. It doesn't matter which hand you use, but many prefer to tap with the dominant hand on the back of the nondominant hand. Keep your head straight with your nose pointed ahead while you do the nine-gamut treatment. Tap about five times for each of the nine gamut positions, while you continue to think of your anxiety or addictive urge throughout the whole series. This step includes eye movements.

While tapping gamut spot on back of hand, do the following:

1. Close your eyes.
2. Open your eyes.
3. Point your eyes way down and way over to the right.
4. Point your eyes way down and way over to the left.
5. Whirl your eyes around in a circle.
6. Whirl your eyes around in the opposite direction.
7. Rest your eyes, and hum any tune—more than just one note (for about five seconds).
8. Count aloud to five.
9. Hum again (important).

Now repeat the tapping under the eyes, collarbone point, under arm, and collarbone point while you think of any remaining urge.

The urge or interest in your particular anxiety or addiction should now be completely gone. If you try to resurrect your urge, you probably won't able to do so. Remember how easy it was to fall into engaging in your anxiety/addictive urge. But this too should have no effect on you, because you have, at least temporarily, eliminated your stress in these areas.

After the treatment, observe how relaxed you feel, the natural relaxation brought on by the removal of an underlying problem. This is normal and healthy, not false and destructive.

Tapping correctly treats the underlying problem causing the anxiety or addictive urge. Although many problems amenable to TFT require only one treatment, addictive urges tend to recur. Because of the ease and expediency of self-treatment, it is simple and practical to keep treating the anxiety/urge.

Once successfully treated, the recurrence of anxiety/urges or any problem is usually due to an *individual energy toxin* (IET). Toxins are a critically important issue for many people and especially for those enmeshed in negative addictive cycles. Toxins often induce a psychological reversal that has the effect of "undoing" or reversing a previously successful treatment and also of interfering or blocking the progress of an incipient treatment. Aside from its impact upon TFT treatments, the effect of psychological reversal is a major factor in many other treatment protocols and can undermine desired goal-oriented motivational states.

How to Correct Psychological Reversal (PR)

Once you do the corrective procedure, and then tap under your eyes again, you should notice a definite (not subtle) and clear reduction in your anxiety/addictive urge.

A psychological reversal exists when a person claims to desire achieving specific goal, but the person's actions and major motivation, as well as their results, appear to be contrary to the professed goal. The person may appear to be striving to achieve (in the *specifically reversed area*), but will instead be significantly or subtly sabotaging the effort.

Psychological reversal can be tested when a person is attuned to a targeted thought field. A field is an invisible, intangible structure in space that has an effect upon matter. A *thought field* is the connection between cognitive awareness and emotions that generates a field that may contain perturbations. For example, for a phobic person, perhaps the thought of getting on an airplane or confronting an insect may generate an intense negative reaction. In such situations, the thought generates a field that contains perturbations (disturbances) responsible for the negative emotions. Testing for the reversal is part of the TFT diagnostic routine administered by trained TFT practitioners. The result is easily determined in a matter of seconds.

Psychological reversals must be corrected for treatment to progress successfully. The corrections involve specific tapping on the side of the hand or under the nose, depending upon when the reversals occur in the treatment sequence. As psychological reversals impede treatment and goal-oriented efforts, correction is a critical element in countering self-sabotaging behavior. Because TFT treatment works so rapidly, psychological reversals are easy to detect and play a key role in determining the success of treatment outcomes. Psychological reversal can be seen in physiology and muscle strength and weakness that people experience when stressed. Lie detection methods measure stress indicators such as heart rate, blood pressure, respiration rate, and GSR (skin response).

From a motivational standpoint, a psychological reversal is a dysfunction in how one's system ought to work. When a person thinks about their aspirations or positive goals, the feelings involved should be strength and health—not weakness and sickness. However, some very intelligent and seemingly highly motivated individuals do not succeed, no matter what program, method of treatment, coaching technique, or educational procedure is used. Many clinicians have noted that certain patients seem to *want* to be ill, or *want* to be disturbed, or even die, even while the patient is actively seeking help. Freud even postulated a death instinct. Others have suggested that most neurotics are self-sabotaging and self-defeating. Some traditional psychoanalytic constructs find parallels with modern neurophysiological findings. But here and now, TFT brings good news even to the most negatively suffering people. We can now fix these "subconscious" obstacles *in seconds* with several specific and sequential taps.

Psychological reversal can be specialized, only affecting certain areas of one's life; or less commonly, it can be wide-reaching and affect much of one's life in a negative way. The incidence of massive reversal is higher in people who have struggled with severe anxiety and addictions or other psychological problems for a long time.

The will, or control over oneself, is definitely limited in a reversed state. The choices available are restricted to negative ones, and the thoughts and ideas tend to have a negative slant. In a severe state of psychological reversal, there is strong resistance to trying or doing the recommended procedures, treatments, or lifestyle changes that would aid in relieving the affliction or symptoms.

The phenomenon of psychological reversal is measurable; its effects are predictable, regular, and scientifically lawful. A person in a state of psychological reversal is unable to respond favorably to an otherwise effective treatment. However, if the reversal is corrected, the person will respond to an effective treatment.

The incidence of psychological reversal varies from problem to problem. For example, anxiety and phobic problems have a reversal incidence of about 40–50 percent. About half of phobic problems are blocked from getting better or completely better. Some may get partially better and then not improve further. But when the TFT treatment for psychological reversal was discovered, the success rate for treating phobias and anxiety immediately increased dramatically. Most previously untreatable phobias became treatable after the simple and fast correction for psychological reversal was administered.

The incidence of psychological reversal is higher among addicts than for any other group. In fact, virtually all addicts suffer from some psychological reversal that is blocking them from getting better. This is why addictions are the most difficult to treat and why so many addicts relapse, even after they seem to be getting better.

The TFT treatment for psychological reversal is simple. The subject must tap on the side of the hand (PR spot) or tap under the nose (See figure) when attuned to the thought in the treatment sequence. Correcting psychological reversals becomes more targeted and effective when the therapist is trained in TFT diagnostic methods.

The Apex Problem

Sometimes, the mind gets in its own way. Many people are familiar with "overthinking" a situation. Another variant of mind games is thinking the wrong way, which usually presents as dismissiveness, or what is known as the *apex problem*. This probably occurs because TFT works so rapidly (and seemingly illogically) that the mind has to make things up in order to avoid dissonance with existing beliefs.

Anyone who does TFT regularly with others is certain to encounter this phenomenon, and needs to understand what is happening. The term is borrowed from Callahan (2002) who cites Koestler (1967), wherein he refers to the operation of the mind at its peak (or apex). The apex problem refers to the commonly observed fact that many people who receive the TFT treatment for any particular problem will *accurately* report the expected and predicted improvement, but *will not typically credit the treatment* for the improvement. They may invoke explanations such as placebo, suggestion, distraction, etc. Dr. Callahan joked that "a placebo is someone else's treatment that works better than yours."

The identification of this phenomenon has basic scientific relevance in that its frequent occurrence leads to a prediction that recipients of treatment may not credit the treatment for the dramatic change of state they report after the treatment—and that many who are successfully treated will invent other explanations in order to avoid the obvious fact of the role of the treatment.

Why this avoidance of acknowledging the obvious efficacy of the treatment? It seems that in order to credit the surprisingly effective treatment, some people diminish cognitive dissonance (with logic) by considering the treatment as a "miracle." Some successfully treated individuals actually say, "It was a miracle!"

TFT does sometimes appear as a kind of miracle (a miracle being something amazing or extraordinary and unexpected, something seemingly contrary to the laws of nature). However, TFT does work according to the laws of nature, including scientific laws. Despite its replicable efficacy, many people have trouble accommodating the seemingly nonlinear effects. Thus many will, after successful treatment, *apex*—either deny the problem they had before the treatment or minimize it, or they will acknowledge that they feel better, but attribute the change to some explanation other than the treatment.

Frequently, people say, "You distracted me from thinking about the problem with that tapping" or "I just can't think about it right now."

When they think about the problem that previously caused severe emotional reaction, they no longer feel any distress or preoccupation about it.

In his "split-brain" experiments, Gazzaniga discovered that the language aspect of the left brain will invent and create "explanations" for phenomena that are introduced to the nonverbal right brain and not known to the left.[13] However, the left brain, observing the behavior, will compulsively "explain" what is taking place, even though there is no basis in fact for the "explanation." It is purely irrelevant invention.

Treated patients never seem to wonder about the possible curative

---

13. Gazzaniga, M. 1985. *The Social Brain*, NY: Basic Books.

role of their surgery, just as the successfully treated addict ignores the role of the therapy they experienced, along with its implied prediction that the treatment will succeed.

Another striking example of the apex problem is in hypnosis—when a good hypnotic subject is given a posthypnotic suggestion with amnesia. The subject may offer irrelevant "explanations" for his behavior because the behavior seems strange to him.

In addiction treatment, the mind is confronted with a phenomenon it can't comprehend, i.e., immediate successful treatment; so the logical "left brain," in Gazzaniga's terms, begins inventing (irrelevant) explanations even though, in the addiction treatment, the brain's hemispheres are intact, and there is no hypnosis nor induced amnesia.

This phenomenon probably occurs in most of us at times, and the commonplace nature of this interesting phenomenon will become obvious to anyone using TFT regularly.

If a person were functioning at or near the apex of the mind, the explanations offered in an apex problem would not be acceptable. The compulsion to invent familiar and effortless explanation appears to override critical thinking.

The speed and stunning effectiveness of TFT treatment seems to generate the apex problem in those vulnerable to it. Nothing that a person has known before could account for the dramatic result. Therefore, many subjects and observers will compulsively *tell* (not ask) why the change took place (i.e., placebo effect, hypnosis, or distraction). That the explainer has never witnessed similar demonstrations of the power of placebo, hypnosis, or distraction appears to carry little weight.

Prior explanations before treatment appear to have little effect upon reducing the apex problem. Perhaps this issue will subside further as TFT and its results become more generally known.

How Long Does It Last?

When the addictive urge, anxiety, or other negative emotion has been significantly reduced or eliminated, a pertinent question is, "How long will the treatment effect last?"

The endurance of the treatment varies from person to person; the time it lasts will even vary for the same person at different times.

In my experience administering thousands of treatments (mostly using Voice Technology, the highest level of TFT which has a success rate of 97 percent for any single treatment), about 80 percent of the people I treat require only one or two treatments to experience successful results that last indefinitely. The other 20 percent have recurrences due mostly to toxins, as described earlier.

Traumas and phobias are among the conditions that Voice Technology with TFT treatment successfully treats with enduring results. Addictions and obsessive-compulsive disorders are refractory (stubborn) and typically require repeated treatment.

Surprisingly, the severity of the problem (according to the dismal success rates of conventional therapies) is not a good predictor of success with TFT. For example, traumas respond exceedingly well to single TFT treatments. One might think that abuse, sexual molestation, war horrors, loss of a loved one, etc., would be so deeply entrenched that little could relieve, much less eliminate these sufferings. Yet using Voice Technology TFT, I have routinely eliminated issues such as these in one treatment.

Among them are the following:

1. A woman who lost her husband and son in a car accident that she survived. She had been depressed by this trauma for nine years.
2. Numerous cases of sexual molestation and childhood abuse.
3. Flashbacks from war experiences.
4. Survivors of Nazi concentration camps.
5. A man traumatized by an incident that occurred a half-century ago, before my single treatment eliminated what had been plaguing him for fifty years.

This is not to suggest that TFT is magic or miraculous, or that it can undo the horrible realities that people endure. Rather, I am stating unequivocally and with solid proof that the emotional sting of these traumatic experiences can be removed completely within minutes.

Returning to the topic of using TFT to help yourself with an array of problems that beset so many people: the success and endurance you experience with TFT will depend on a number of factors:

1. The degree of psychological reversal.
2. One's sensitivity to toxins.
3. Correct implementation of the procedures and persistence in repetition, when necessary.
4. One's general health.
5. The nature (typically not severity) of the problem being treated.

Notice here that one's *belief* in the efficacy of the treatment is not listed as a factor in predictive success. This is because *it does not matter*. Like an antibiotic, TFT will either work or it won't, *irrespective of one's beliefs*. One simply has to administer it.

Admittedly, self-help treatment is not as effective as professional treatment for more complex cases. However, self-help treatment has the advantages of being free, convenient, and private—and they do often work splendidly. So why not try it?

There are no negative side effects with TFT. The only downside to self-help treatment is that if you don't get satisfactory results quickly, you may give up, dismiss TFT, and pass up an extremely valuable tool for living intact, simply because you didn't get significant relief the first or second time. This is why I suggest contacting a professional when a self-administered procedure does not appear to be working. Be aware of how TFT works, how it differs in practice and theory from conventional treatments, and how the apex problem can lead you astray.

The vast majority of people will experience profound calmness and significant reduction in anxiety, urges and cravings the first and every time they use the TFT algorithms. A small minority of people can do just one urge-reduction treatment and never have a further desire for their addictive substance. This, alas, is a rare response, but it does happen.

For most people, cravings will return at the first sign of stress, and it is imperative to repeat the treatment each time an urge arises. Frequency of treatment depends upon the degree of stress. Keep in mind that repeated treatments are not wasted—rather, each administration of the procedure treats the underlying cause of the addiction problem. Since the underlying problem is addressed and treated, rather than being masked as with tranquilizers, the repeated treatments may also eventually eliminate the underlying problem. Aside from toxins and psychological reversal, many problems undergirded by negative emotions contain multiple thought fields. The resurfacing of negative emotions, once handily treated, often indicates other thought fields that need treatment. A skilled TFT practitioner is adept at helping patients identify and target relevant perturbed thought fields.

Levels of TFT Treatment

The three levels of treatment in TFT are algorithms, causal diagnosis, and Voice Technology.

Algorithms are "summary recipes" for administering TFT that have resulted from applying the commonalities of thousands of individually diagnosed perturbation sequences. Algorithms are what nonprofessionals typically use to treat themselves (finger tapping, etc.).

Causal diagnosis is the objective scientific procedure of identifying perturbations (specific to particular thought fields) and determining which tapping points and in what order will be most effective in *collapsing the perturbations*—that is, decoding or deprogramming the thought field so that the perturbations that cause the disturbance are no longer active.

Causal diagnosis involves a combination of having the person *attune* the thought field and then using variations of applied kinesiology (muscle testing) to identify the active perturbations. The practitioner typically does this by "testing" various points on the patient's body.

Voice Technology (VT) is the practice of diagnosing the points through information provided by the person's voice. This is the most advanced level of TFT, and it offers a number of advantages including the obvious expediency of treating someone effectively by phone. Voice Technology is also quicker and often more precise in treating patients with greater complexity or long strings of perturbations. VT is also expedient in the identification of toxins that may cause psychological reversals and interfere with treatment. Toxins, the substances that cause a psychological reversal and may block or reverse the effects of successful treatment, typically include various foods, toiletries, aromas, and supplements that act are toxic to a percentage of people. For many, the sustained positive effects of treatments and better health require the identification of and abstention from toxins.

Nature encodes the sources of distress and their solutions within our bodies and minds. Because of nature's recapitulation and signaling system, the human voice indicates with precision the causes of emotional and physical disturbance and can be used in tandem with Thought Field Therapy to eliminate the source and symptoms in minutes.

Applications of TFT Treatment

TFT is useful for eliminating a wide array of problems. By eliminating negative emotions with consistency, a new world will unfold—a world of personal freedom in which a person can set their mind to achieve some goal, identify the emotional traps that so heavily and surreptitiously disrupt their well-being, and impede their purposefully desired behavior, and attain one goal after another as they progress on to a better life, free from the shackles of anxiety and its cohorts.

A partial list of negative emotions you can eliminate with TFT:

- Anxiety
- Depression
- Frustration
- Anger
- Feeling overwhelmed
- Stress
- Irritation
- Impatience
- Fear
- Embarrassment
- Guilt
- Hopelessness
- Rejection

- Grief
- Hurt
- Worrying
- Cravings
- Disgust
- Emotional and behavioral overreactions
- Jealousy and lovesickness

As you gain success with eliminating these unwanted negative emotions, you can use TFT along with other skills and techniques to meet and overcome the other challenges:

- Procrastination
- Addictions
- Bad habits
- Behavior problems
- Sleep problems
- Obsessiveness and compulsiveness
- Weight and appetite control
- Eating disorders
- Study habits
- Relationship dysfunction
- Avoidance
- Phobias and fears
- Habitual worrying
- Negative thinking
- Choking under pressure
- Self-defeating attitudes
- Fatigue
- Jet lag
- Finishing projects

An expedient tool I developed for self-treatment is found in a video series accessible on my website: https://marksteinberg.com /tapping/?access=granted

CHAPTER 12

EEG Neurofeedback: Train the Brain

Brain Function: the Inside Story

As discussed earlier, *self-regulation* is a term that describes how the brain manages our internal neurological affairs by channeling and integrating the firing of brain neurons: our interior EEG (electroencephalogram). This ordinary biological function is complex, elegant, intricate, and subject to many influences that can disrupt or *dysregulate* neurological function, which can cause many types of physiological and psychological problems. Developing and maintaining stable self-regulation is vital to reducing anxiety and keeping it at bay.

Along with its sensitivity, our brain is capable of adjustments. The brain's plasticity allows it to grow and change, and modify and improve its functioning. The powerful structure that sits atop our shoulders is a marvelous control center, governing how we feel and operate. To maximize its effectiveness, the brain needs valid real-time information in order to balance, stabilize, and regulate.

Just as we see visually by looking outward (needing a mirror to see what's on our back), we process neurologically without direct access to the network of neurons firing inside our brain.

Fortunately, we have a noninvasive and effective method for delving inside our brain to observe, monitor, and modify (if necessary) the firing of neurons and the flow of important information that affects our self-regulation. This method, called neurofeedback or EEG biofeedback (or simply neurofeedback or biofeedback) is a proven scientific technique that has been researched and practiced clinically for more than a half century. The use of neurofeedback is highly successful in diminishing anxiety and other psychological and physiological symptoms. The method of "training" our brainwaves improves our brain function and self-regulation, promoting better emotional and cognitive functioning. The process works without chemicals and, when practiced over even a short time, induces beneficial and enduring results.

Reimagine the Brain

Imagine a "device" that could control how we feel, how alert or tired we are, and whether other people, disappointments, frustrations, and setbacks perturb us. What if this device allowed us to turn up pleasure and turn down pain? Further, what if we could use this device to recall the past, plan into the future, and record and edit in five of our sensory modalities? Even better, imagine that this device could communicate with other such devices, run on its own energy, and recharge itself by simply going to sleep. Well, each of us actually has immediate access to this remarkable piece of equipment: our marvelous brain!

This extraordinary tool is a power-packed onboard computer with amazing capabilities to manage and regulate all the systems in our body. Our brain is the portal through which we experience and respond to life. Our brain is a delicately balanced, multifaceted instrument that interprets and reacts to challenges; and the manner in which it accomplishes this directly determines the extent to which we are able to live well.

We must nurture, protect, and nourish our brain by taking a deliberate and proactive role in developing its full range of capabilities. Ways to achieve this vital objective include intentionally keeping our brain vibrant through learning, analyzing and solving problems, and performing mental exercises that "stretch" our brain's capabilities.

Even such mundane pursuits as doing a crossword puzzle, reading a book, playing chess or Scrabble, or doing research on the internet are deliberate "brain-feeding" pursuits.

Throughout the day and night, our brain is activated and deactivated as we interact with our outside environment and our own internal circuitry. The activity in our brain encompasses a series of physical processes that affect our thoughts, emotions, hormonal secretions, and vascular and muscle activity. Our brain determines whether we like something, and how we will react to it. This stimulus/reaction dynamic even includes how our digestive system reacts to specific foods.

Of course, our brain is not an autocrat, but only acts in response to those areas within the body or our environment that send it signals. If we stub a toe or eat something that our body doesn't tolerate well, our brain will be notified by the particular stimulus, and we experience pain and discomfort. These physical sensations are nervous system responses that influence the brain's narrative. The brain's narrative is the interpretive sum of what is perceived, evoked, and imprinted as we respond to life's machinations. . Mental attitudes, awareness, and physical states are inextricably intertwined. Our states of arousal greatly affect our perceptions, what our mind says about them, and our relationship with them. However, these elements are not preordained, nor are they immutable; and we can take charge of our experiences and choices in a number of ways.

If you could train your brain to take charge in the ways that you want, what would you choose to do? Alleviate physical or emotional pain? Focus and organize more productively? Get more restful sleep? Reduce anger, irritation, fear, or procrastination? Banish addictions and compulsions? Become more compassionate? Eliminate anxiety?

The good news is that we can train our brain to accomplish such things and much more. We can achieve improved levels of self-regulation, self-control, performance enhancement, cognitive focus, and emotional well-being. EEG neurofeedback (also called EEG biofeedback) is the method—a procedure for training our brain (with the use of a computer) that teaches our mind and body how to function better.

The method works relatively quickly—within days for some people, and within months for others. EEG neurofeedback uses the same principles that nature allows us to grow and heal: principles that permeate the physical world and universe—the principles of *timing*.

Timing mechanisms form the basis of physics as well as biology. Our DNA contains timing information that controls growth and development (and possibly the onset of disease and breakdown). The timing of our brain and nervous system determines whether we are impulsive, impatient, sleepy, and whether we understand something. By training (or tuning) the timing mechanisms in our brain and nervous system, we can use nature's principles to influence states of being and correct ailments and impairments that derail the ability to live intact. EEG neurofeedback can effectively initiate and enable a healing process and allow us to harness our brain's capabilities and potential.

What Is EEG Neurofeedback?

Neurofeedback is training in self-regulation, a natural process that is a necessary part of good brain function. Self-regulation training permits the brain and central nervous system function more capably, efficiently, and proficiently by taking advantage of the brain's *plasticity*, or ability to adapt. EEG neurofeedback directly trains our brainwaves through the use of computers and specific, carefully calibrated software.[14] Our electrical brain activity is measured by the electroencephalogram, or EEG.

During neurofeedback training, the client (with practitioner guidance) observes the brain in action from moment to moment. This information is shown on a computer screen and simultaneously rewards the brain for changes toward more appropriate patterns in its activity, as it affects and conditions any measurable aspect of brain function.

Though working with a trained professional is important when beginning neurofeedback, some people eventually perform their own training by obtaining their own equipment and applying the learning on themselves—similar to practicing at a gym with a trainer and then acquiring home equipment. This is a gradual learning process.

Neurofeedback works by monitoring our brainwaves and converting

---

14. . EEG biofeedback is the training of brainwaves. Another more localized and limited type of biofeedback, called EMG biofeedback (electromyogram) is used to train specific muscles.

the electrical signals (EEG) from your head into filtered digital information that is then used to modulate a video game on a computer screen. To do this, electrode sensors are attached to the scalp with a benign adhesive. Nothing goes into the head via these wires—neither electric current nor information. The sensors simply monitor and conduct the signal from the head and brain to an amplifier, and from there to one or more computers. Computer equipment digitally transforms the brain signals into audiovisual information, usually presented in the form of entertaining and engaging games. While our brain is being trained, we "play" the game for about thirty minutes at a time by actually controlling it with our brainwaves. The marvel of electronics makes this possible, but the key to its efficacy lies in the technology of filtering our brainwaves, and in the science of selecting the range of signals that our brain needs to alter in order to feel and function better.

The feedback we get happens when the game goes better, seemingly on its own. Actually, we control the game by producing more of the brainwave activity promoted by the bandwidths that are selected by the therapist to optimize brain function. The process where the brain is subtly influenced and coached to make more of certain brainwaves and fewer of others is, in part, a form of *operant conditioning*—a behavioral term for the strategic use of reinforcement that conditions (trains) the brain and nervous system in a safe, subtle, and persistent way. When our actions are reinforced, they are strengthened so they are more likely to occur. It is similar to praising a child for positive behaviors with the result that those behaviors become more probable..

However, because the operant conditioning model does not account for the vast transforming changes that routinely occur with a newer *infra-low frequency neurofeedback* (ILF-neurofeedback) training modality called *endogenous neuromodulation,* we have advanced our understanding of the way the brain integrates its own information as it observes it in real time. This model is characterized by the absence the discrete reinforcers (a distinguishing feature of the operant conditioning model) and still relies on a complementary inhibiter design that targets different levels and steps in the process. But the markers used only tell us the state of the brain's dysregulation. Any response to this information, including any prescription for change, is left to the discretion of the brain. The principle of endogenous neuromodulation extends to the responses to the brain-derived signal, leaving responses entirely to the discretion of the person's brain. Consider this guiding principle from neuroscientist Paul Bach-y-Rita: "If you give the brain any information about itself, it will make sense out of it."

The reinforcement effects of operant conditioning still apply, though not directly in the agency process of presenting the brain with its own real-time dynamic information. As the brain monitors, adjusts, and improves self-regulation, greater internal functioning and modulation occurs, and the brain transitions to *practice* more of its newfound regulation balance and homeostasis. This results in new perceptions, new adaptive habits, improved attitudes and expectations, and augmented flexibility. The practice of better self-regulation becomes the brain's "new normal." This new functioning is reinforced through the repetition of more adaptive habits and the inherent and external rewards experienced as a result of improved brain and behavioral functioning.

The fundamental distinction between operant conditioning and endogenous neuromodulation is that the former is only capable of engaging with macroscopic phenomena—operant conditioning can only work well when the rewarded events stick out above normal variability of the signal. But good regulation is a matter of great subtlety, and that is only available in feedback via endogenous neuromodulation.

Using an exercise model relevant to neurofeedback as "taking your brain to the gym neurologically," we can become more fit by subjecting our body to the gradual structured challenges of physical exercise. Our body adapts and gradually becomes stronger, more durable, more flexible, and more resilient with easier recovery. When we challenge our heart, lungs, and muscles, we are not rewarding new or learned behaviors per se, we are simply inducing and strengthening physiological responses. However, the practice and cumulative effects of this process undoubtedly result in more practice, improved functioning and health, better lifestyle habits, changes in outlook and self-care, and a host of other lasting benefits. Those are the direct effects. The secondary effects indeed conform to the learning model described by operant conditioning.

Practice with neurofeedback training, in essence, allows the brain to witness its own patterns, and *endogenous neuromodulation* facilitates enduring changes, which the brain and the environment reinforce.

As the technology has steadily improved, advances have occurred in the subjective user experience and in the training and development of deep neural networks that govern functioning. At the user level, different forms of entertainment, such as commercial movies and various videos, are used, such that the EEG brainwave information is livestreamed seamlessly and blended with the entertainment so that the viewer witnesses brain activity moment by moment through digital special effects.

At the level of neurological influence (the agency of training effect), advanced development of these techniques allows for improvement beyond the operant conditioning effect by tapping into deeper neural network rhythms that show brainwave patterns at *infra-low* levels as basic as one ten thousandth of a hertz (Hz).[15]

This level of brain observation has extremely powerful effects on positively modifying brain flexibility and enhancing the ability to control fight-or-flight response at the autonomic level and to heal trauma without language or restimulation. While playing the game or watching a movie or video, we are being reinforced neurologically at the rate of approximately three thousand "rewards" per session as our brain is being shown how to adjust its timing mechanisms to more functional and "feel good" levels. All we have to do is sit in a comfortable chair and observe the computer screen. Our job in the training process is to bear witness to our own brain activity. The process is fascinating! But how does this exercise help us overcome challenges, symptoms, illnesses, setbacks, and the conflict that results from living in a difficult world?

---

15. EEG activity is measured in physic terminology where frequency refers to the number of complete rhythmic cycles per second. Mammals have many frequency ranges. Typically, we measure frequencies between 0-3 Hz (sleepy waves) and 50-100 Hz (physically strenuous activity or fight-or-flight bursts). *Infra-low* activity occurs simultaneously and is more fundamental to self-regulatory functions and the brain's programming and projection of future activity. The elongated time period to complete each cycle (hours to days) allows the brain to witness patterns of biological activity otherwise unavailable to conscious observation (e.g., compare to electron microscopes facilitating observation of cell structures).

How Neurofeedback Works

Neurofeedback is essentially biofeedback applied directly by the brain. We are actually observing our brain in action from moment to moment, using specialized computer equipment that reflects our brain's performance as this is happening. The electrode sensors conduct signals from our scalp to the sensitive equipment that digitally filters and transforms those signals into entertaining video games that the person controls, just by observing the game on the screen. Unlike most video games, we don't use our hands to control the game. The essential game activity and progress is controlled by our brainwaves. As we play the game, our brain is rewarded for changing its own activity to more appropriate patterns. This is a gradual learning process that applies to any measurable aspect of brain function.

Many conditions that detract from health and happiness are caused by a brain and nervous system that is *dysregulated*, causing the brain to be inconsistent in its "housekeeping" functions and to wander into activity that does not suit the demands of the situation. Neurofeedback uses the brain's natural bioelectrical rhythms to self-correct that wandering.

Think of the process as teaching the brain and nervous system to stay consistently within a lane while driving on a road and navigating different speeds, terrains, and conditions. Or consider how you balance a bicycle by blending your brain's vestibular function with sensory and motor feedback from changing conditions and gravity's guidance. Verbal instruction or logical thinking are not what induces these capacities. Rather, we develop these capacities by training our brain to monitor and focus its attention on the relevant events, both inside our mind and outside in the environment. In so doing, the brain makes necessary adjustments—automatically, continuously, and without strain—in the same way as you would in steering a car or balancing a bicycle. The process becomes a natural interplay of subconscious and conscious influences.

In the EEG neurofeedback training procedure, the process of learning "how to make different brainwaves" occurs as the brain adjusts and interprets the cause-and-effect relationship between its own activity and the resultant video game responses.

The beauty of neurofeedback is that it makes this cause-and-effect relationship easily observable and accessible—as simple as noticing when a variety of elements on the screen appear and disappear, go faster or slower, or when sounds become more frequent, rhythmic, or melodic. Games can range from fast moving, stimulating, and sleek (such as car or spaceship games) to quiet and calming games (such as those with flowers, bubbles, and music).

Many games appeal easily to children's natural abilities. Because the games are nonverbal, even very young and severely impaired children can engage with them successfully. For example, in some games, geometric shapes on the screen become bigger or smaller, objects are positioned higher or lower, and sounds go on or off. Following such cues is easy and natural, since we develop the basic perceptual skills that are required by the age of two. A key feature to the efficacy of neurofeedback is that the games are interactive with the nervous system, not with logic, achievement, language, or other higher cognitive skills. I have trained blind people by using only sound feedback and deaf people by using only visual feedback. The brain is keenly sensitive in seeking information through available channels.

The brain characteristics of critical importance involve the various brainwave frequencies (electrical cycles per second). These "carry" information from one part of the brain to another, much like radio signals carry information from the transmitter towers to a radio. A natural ebb and flow in this activity is detected by sensitive computer instrumentation. The information about the preferred brainwaves is represented within the game itself. For instance, larger brainwaves may appear as a larger box or a wider bar on the screen. Or they may advance the spaceship or slow it down.

Remarkably, the brain can easily figure out what is required to make the game go just as you can determine that steering a wheel to the left will make a car turn in that direction. You make the game advance just by watching the screen; the brain likes continuity and will alter its brainwaves in order to keep the game "going." Eventually, the brain learns and continues the key elements and subtleties. The neurofeedback software uses inhibit thresholds that simultaneously show the brain when it is engaging in "out-of-control" activity. Eventually, you achieve control of your brainwaves through making these changes happen on the computer screen. This improved control translates into more appropriate and functional behaviors in everyday living.

The distinguishing features of neurofeedback are that it:

- Initiates learning at a neurological level—training brain behavior that we may not feel strongly connected to, and that we may not feel particular responsibility for. When brain behavior is normalized, outward behavior naturally follows. Eventually, life becomes more manageable, often with little additional conscious effort.

- Makes a person a witness to their own brain in action. You can watch it meander from success to struggle and back again. The neurofeedback process teaches you about your own visible behavior while, simultaneously, your brain is learning about itself in a unique and replicable way.

- Accelerates learning and modifies behavior rapidly and efficiently (producing up to three thousand reinforcements per session).

- Develops brain abilities that translate to other life situations because these abilities are fundamental, allowing the brain to remain calm, organized, and focused, whereas otherwise it might escalate into too much excitability or lapse into disorganization.

How EEG Neurofeedback Can Help

Our brain is the master control for all the systems in our body—the vehicle through which we perceive and experience "being"—cerebral, emotional, and spiritual. Because neurofeedback trains and fine-tunes our brain capacities, it is an effective intervention for a broad array of problems and conditions.

Some challenges that respond well to neurofeedback:

- Attention problems, including ADD and ADHD
- Moodiness and serious mood disorders (such as bipolar disorder)
- Behavior problems and disorders
- Sleep problems
- Learning problems
- Autistic spectrum and pervasive developmental delay
- Aspergers syndrome
- Head injury and brain injury
- Seizures and subclinical seizure activity
- Birth trauma
- Headaches and migraines
- Teeth grinding
- Anxiety and depression
- Addictions
- Bed-wetting and soiling
- Nightmares and night terrors
- Sleepwalking and sleep talking
- Sleep apnea
- Obsessiveness and compulsions
- Tics and Tourette's syndrome
- PMS and menopause
- Antisocial behavior
- Stroke
- Tremors and restless leg
- Fears and worries
- Eating disorders
- Weight and appetite control
- Study habits
- Recovery from surgery and anesthesia
- Chronic pain
- Anger
- Language disorders

- Indifference and motivation problems
- Oversensitivity and lack of sensitivity
- Muscular coordination
- Memory issues

EEG Neurofeedback and Secrets to Living Intact

In my book, *Living Intact: Challenge and Choice in Tough Times*, I define, explain, and explore the concepts of *living intact* and *choice*. An excerpt explains these terms:

One factor is shared in common: we live out our days, balancing on the fulcrum that separates survival on one side from meaning on the other, facing challenges and seeking to secure, reinforce, refine, and enhance those aspects of life we hold dear. I call this dynamic process the drive for *Living Intact*.

Living Intact is an active and systematic engagement with life's challenges, using the potential of the challenge process to resolve the inherent breakdowns, dissatisfactions, and discrepancies that result from our desires for what life should be and our actual experiences living life.

Choice is the continuing opportunity to individuate and form an identity, to exercise being you, to make a difference, and to make your mark on historical events.

Self-control, proper sensitivity, flexibility, awareness, and the functional use of our life challenges are endemic to implementing the best practices for an intact life. Neurofeedback is a highly effective method for developing and refining these qualities in people of all ages and functional levels. Though the brains of senior citizens and toddlers may be quite different, young brains and older brains respond well to the learning and healing that neurofeedback facilitates.

Older people can benefit in a variety of ways, from improved sleep and memory to relief from pain, irritability, and depression. Children of all ages benefit because neurofeedback catalyzes the developmental processes, helping children to learn more quickly and efficiently and helping to normalize and mature neurological functioning. Because neurofeedback is so effective at improving concentration, focus, and response to challenge, it is an ideal adjunct to achieving peak performance levels in many areas of life: athletics, academics, business, art and music, research, and relationships.

By training the brain, we become more self-regulated, and this leads to better self-control. We can concentrate better and focus on outcomes and goals more effectively. Because neurofeedback develops brain and nervous system response, we will become more flexible and less prone to unwanted excitability and overreactions. As we progress further, our mind and body will recover more easily and fully from stress, and we'll be less likely to depart into "excursions" of brain activity that promote and sustain negative emotions. This process builds upon itself. As we become less likely to fall victim to brainwave excursions and overreactions, we are likely to become more compassionate and empathetic.

Remember that developing and exercising compassion is key to living intact. This ability is vital in establishing healthy and reasonable self-control. Fluency in compassion helps us deliberately alter the probability of a particular outcome. Compassion serves not only to reduce aggression and to salve social friction, but also to fashion a reality check on whether a tendency to magnify, distort, or misperceive may be causing us to overreact.

On a practical level, self-directed and other-directed compassion are all-purpose tools that soften the harshness and stings of life. Self-directed compassion gives us the flexibility to accept and adjust to the things we cannot change, the parts of life that do not go our way. It gives us the strength to tolerate adversity, rejection, and all manner of hardship. Other-directed compassion creates a context for tolerance and forbearance.

How EEG Neurofeedback Develops Compassion

To understand how brainwave training can make us more compassionate, we need some basic information on how the brain processes emotion and thought. The substructures of the human brain are housed in left and right hemispheres that function distinctly and interactively. Many people have one hemisphere that is underdeveloped or functioning in a compromised manner. Factors such as genetics, deprivation, faulty learning, and injury can stunt or alter the development of empathy and compassion, as well as other important functions.

The brain's right hemisphere does most of the processing of emotional information and primitive (sub)brain perception and response. When this hemisphere is functioning with limited capacity, the results can include anger, impulsivity, insensitivity, aggression, overt selfishness, irritability, and the inhibition of empathy and compassion.

Neurofeedback training calms the brain and sensitizes the right hemisphere appropriately. This is essential to reducing anxiety. With this training, people become more amicable and socially appropriate, more understanding, and more empathetic. Emotional sensitivity and compassion go hand in hand with perceptual awareness and a reduction in the fight-or-flight response that so often keeps the right hemisphere vigilant, distant, and defensive.

When a person does neurofeedback training, the people in their life often report that the person has become far less argumentative and much more cooperative. The neurofeedback trainee is often reported to "lose interest" in arguing, resulting in less-frequent and less-intense opposition and quarrels. This turnabout is sometimes described as "having the wind go out of the sails" in the middle of a dispute, wherein the trainee gives up trying to dominate and prevail. By contrast, motivation and persistence toward productive and cooperative endeavors simultaneously increases.

Physiological states greatly influence and construct our mental narrative. The mind's narrative reflects its ability and habit of creating a constantly adapting "story" to accommodate our passions, beliefs, momentary emotions, and internal state of arousal. Our mind uses an internal language that narrates thoughts, opinions, perceptions, and feelings. This narrative is always switched on, interpreting events, giving opinions, cracking jokes, making sarcastic comments, discussing feelings, passing evaluations, and announcing upcoming intentions and anticipations. When this internal dialogue and incessant chatter become loud and dissonant, it is difficult to feel calm.

Even if dialogue and chatter are noisy or uncomfortable, the narrative serves a useful purpose in that it helps maintain a cohesive and sequential story about what is going on. The narrative is the descriptive embodiment of the characteristics we identify with as our "self." When this self becomes threatened or *perceives* a threat, we experience a reaction that combines visceral physiological response (usually heightened arousal) with emotional sensation. If a threat is perceived, the attached emotions are always negative. This is an instinctive response, and sometimes it can save us. Most often however, negative emotions are an overreaction and an unfortunate, adverse response to a challenge. Defenses are mounted, and the mind begins to concoct its story that is designed to protect itself and justify the nervous system's reaction.

One of my patients aptly described her narrative as the "hamster wheel" that keeps spinning and going nowhere. She was delighted when neurofeedback calmed her mind and let the hamster rest.

A metaphor to describe the neuropsychological aspects of hemispheric coordination might be the juxtaposition of "text" and "context." The left hemisphere deals more with text, and the right hemisphere deals more with context. That is, the left hemisphere controls language, logic, linear cause-and-effect reasoning, symbology, and sequence, whereas the right hemisphere controls nonverbal processing, body image and perception, spatial reasoning, emotional tone, and the background setting and relative importance of individual bits of information streaming into the filters of the brain.

This is a simplified model. Brain functioning is complex, and therefore, neurofeedback operates on the complexities of the brain by using biological and physical principles that take advantage of the brain's inherent plasticity. However, for the purpose of communicating how it is possible (and routine) to develop compassion, interest and ability for intimacy, and more mature sensitivity, be assured that when the left hemisphere improves focus and sequential processing and the right hemisphere calms down and self-regulates, that hamster stops running and gnawing, and the needs and interests of other people become more apparent and attractive.

Neurofeedback and Challenge

It may seem astonishing that we can play video games with our brainwaves and positively change our life. However, neurofeedback is so powerful and effective because it utilizes the *challenge principle* in asking and guiding our brain to step up. Actually, neurofeedback is what taught me this principle, and I have been integrating and expanding it ever since my first encounter with this magnificent technique.

The essence of neurofeedback is that it challenges our brain continuously. Professionals in the field of neurotherapy often refer to this challenge process as "appealing to the brain" to engage in slightly different activity. The mechanism of neurofeedback is that it filters brainwave signals and selects only portions of them to reinforce. As the computers filter the signals produced by our brain, the video game "asks" us to make more of certain brainwave activity and less of other activity simultaneously. The "asking" or "appealing" takes the form of rewarding our brain when we do so and ignoring it when we do not.

The process is gentle, subtle, relentless, compelling, and efficacious. Neurofeedback uses only reward—no punishment. It works both consciously and subconsciously. Easy and yet challenging, enticing and boring, emotionless and yet evoking emotion, in a non-adversarial, nonthreatening way, neurofeedback "nudges" the brain toward less familiar angles and levels. And the brain—less accustomed to these new impingements—pushes back. This helpful "push-back" response elicits and strengthens adaptive responses to challenge and increase flexibility.

Think of physical training as an analogy. When you tax your muscles and cardiovascular system, they "push back" with greater strength and endurance. Indeed, I call neurofeedback the core of *mental fitness training* (Steinberg and Othmer, 2004). Unlike physical training however, most people experience lasting change after a sufficient amount of neurofeedback training without the need for constant up-keep. This is because neurofeedback takes advantage of the brain's ability to change its *timing mechanisms*—the various frequencies at which nerve cells fire.

Timing mechanisms are fundamental to the scientific underpinnings of the natural universe. Planets move, seasons change, babies are born, genetic patterns unfold, aging occurs, food grows, and people communicate and problem solve all according to timing mechanisms. The key role of the brain lies in communication. Communication is all about timing. The brain's internal timing mechanisms have to work faster than anything else that the brain is asked to do. And when the brain operates at "brain speed," it is also subject to failure. These failures can be of two kinds: a hard failure, such as a lapse into coma; or soft failures, where we just don't function as well as we might. The "soft" failures are the domain of neurofeedback. When you change your brain via neurofeedback, you are utilizing the mechanism nature gave you to modify and adapt, the same mechanism by which your brain learned how to behave in the first place. Isn't that incredible?

Figuring Things Out without Reason

Some problems require conscious thought and planning, and others tend to be more automatic. When you know how to ride a bicycle, you don't have to calculate the degrees of leaning or turning in order to keep your balance in real time. Amazingly, but not surprisingly, you are monitoring internal gyroscopic body sensations while simultaneously reacting and adjusting to terrain changes, all the while steering and controlling the bicycle. The conditions are constantly changing, yet you are almost effortlessly adapting in real time—and the process is usually fun!

Our brain problem solves continuously at many levels, whether we are sleeping, waking, or somewhere in between. Responding to internal and external challenges continuously, and modulating and integrating what's going on inside and outside, our brain is a 24/7 challenge-and-change detector.

Our brain responds to body signals that indicate what we need very soon (such as thirst, temperature change, or pain relief), and sooner or later (such as desires for certain foods that our body knows will supply needed nutrients). Our brain tells us in subtle ways that we need contact with certain individuals or perhaps to pay attention to particular issues. Additionally, our brain is the filtering device for spiritual and creative stirrings. Many of these signals result from something other than logical reason or cause-and-effect analysis.

Neurofeedback takes advantage of the brain's ability to problem solve, figure things out, and strengthen itself, even when we are not consciously dictating what to do. Neurofeedback facilitates this process by using electrical signals and the biophysics of nature to challenge the brain in ways that almost always produce highly desirable results.

Biophysics and Blessings

Neurofeedback modifies brain activity using three principal mechanisms:

1. Encouraging or reinforcing the brain to produce brainwaves that are helpful and relevant to desired outcome states,

2. Discouraging or extinguishing brainwaves that interfere with desired outcome states, and

3. Presenting the brain with specific challenges designed to train particular brain areas to strengthen, problem solve, and communicate better with each other.

Encourage or reinforce your brain to produce brainwaves

The nuts and bolts of neurofeedback training comprise how the procedure encourages the brain to make greater *amplitudes* (strength of the signal) at particular frequencies (electrical cycles per second). The computers that process the signals emanating from the brain extract information about particular brainwave frequencies. The video game continuously shows the ebb and flow of this activity. As you play the game, you are automatically changing the activity levels of different brainwave frequencies. Eventually, your brainwave activity is "shaped" toward more desirable and more regulated performance. The frequencies we target, and the specific locations on the scalp where we "listen in" on the brain, are specific to the conditions we are trying to address. These are specific to each individual.

By promoting greater production of amplitudes at certain frequencies, we teach our brain to gravitate toward more functional states, and to maintain these states as is useful and appropriate to varying situations. People prefer different names for these states—such as "being in the zone," "putting on your game face," "chilling out," and so forth—but the basic idea is that you learn to *activate* and *deactivate* your brainwave activity to suit the situation. The training on the computer generalizes to varying real-life circumstances, much as weight training or running might generalize to heightened fitness that allows us to meet the physical demands and challenges of daily activities.

Discourage or extinguish brainwaves that interfere

In tandem with teaching our brain to make more of the brainwaves associated with desirable outcomes, neurofeedback discourages the brain's excursion into dysfunctional states. These excursions may be so brief that they are unobservable in overt behavior. Rather, we infer them from the existence of certain patterns in the EEG. Such excursions, however, are rare. The coupling of overt behavior and EEG "behavior" is so intimate that the production of anomalous brainwave patterns interferes with desired outcome states. The neurofeedback procedure accomplishes control over such excursions by inhibiting the reward (forward motion, points, sounds, etc.) on the video game. In particular, this modality teaches the brain to avoid significant *departures* from the functional flow of activity that suits a particular brain state. This abstract-sounding process is really a simple principle, ingenuously applied to neurobiology via the miracle blending of digital technology, learning theory, and the brilliance of devoted engineering.

Think of the process as though you are driving on the freeway with sensors attached that allow you to drift slightly within a lane, to change lanes gradually, and to slow down and speed up within a range of allowable speeds. However, should you suddenly veer way out beyond the freeway lanes or slow down or accelerate in a manner that posed danger, the system would notify you and diminish fuel supply to the engine until you regained control.

Another analogy: in baseball, a runner is allowed a lenient margin of sideways drift when running from one base to another. Veering too far outside of rule-based limits is not allowed, and the player must touch each base in order to progress.

A significant feature of this *inhibition of rewards* (inhibition of continuous movement) process is that no punishment is involved. The reward is simply cut off until the person regains control and resumes progress within the allowable margins. This process is supportive and efficient, since people generally do not learn as well under conditions of punishment or stress.

Remember, neurofeedback is usually attempting to teach brains that are already stressed. We don't learn to drive well by having multiple accidents. Rather, we master the process of adapting to changing conditions via the gentle persistent nudges in the right direction provided by correct practice and subtly noticeable reminders of when we exceed limits (such as the bumps in the lane stripes).

The inhibit features of neurofeedback training are especially helpful to those individuals who struggle with an unstable brain that routinely deregulates into overreactive electrical activity. For example, people with seizures, intractable anxiety, migraines, cerebral irritability, and other conditions are prone to this disruptive brain activity without being aware of it. By bringing it into subliminal awareness without the penalty of symptoms or censure, neurofeedback allows the brain to self-correct its own aberrations in a manner that is natural, comfortable, and enduring.

Psychotropic medications do this "by force," acting as a kind of neurochemical "cruise control" guided by time release (and the approximate judgment of the prescribing physician). A problem with the medication approach is that, in the interests of short-term economy and collision prevention, it can add unpleasant side effects and sacrifices the autonomy and flexibility of "driver-guided" control.

Present the brain with specific challenges

Basic models of neurofeedback training have used the first two principles for decades with cumulative and far-reaching efficacy; many practitioners continue to succeed with these models. However, in recent years, neurofeedback scientists have significantly increased its success with the challenge model. The emphasis on two aspects of neurofeedback interaction with brain function has quickened and deepened the effects when the brain is challenged by a task, and learns to "push back," and becomes more capable.

A remarkable advance is the neurofeedback training of *phase relationships* between brain sites. Another extraordinary innovation is the introduction of *infra-low frequency* (ILF) reward-based training.

It's Not Just a Phase

To appreciate these innovations, it is helpful to understand some mathematical principles of physics and electrical signals. *Phase* refers to the timing relationship of two electrical cycles operating independently. As a practical matter, the parameter of phase is useful only when the two cycles are operating at the same or nearly the same frequency. But this happens to be precisely the situation when the brain is organizing communication between two locations on the scalp. These two regions have to be attuned to each other, much like the radio station and the receiver.

When an electrode is placed on the scalp, it samples the signal coming from that area (site) and displays the information as a cycle ranging from a peak of +1 to -1. The height or depth of the wave is measured in *microvolts* (millionths of a volt) and displayed in an undulating line a certain number of times per second. For example, a brainwave pattern of 12 Hz at 75 microvolts would mean that there are twelve up-and-down complete wave patterns each second. Each cycle would include a peak of +1 and a nadir of -1 at its particular amplitude (See Figure 1). The point at which the waveform crosses from plus to minus in each cycle can be assigned the phase value of zero (See Figure 1). Phase values for each waveform vary continuously and smoothly until the wave undergoes a complete cycle, and then it repeats.

Figure 1

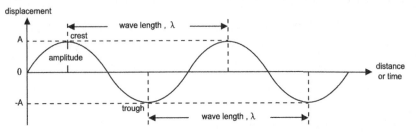

The first two principal mechanisms described explain how neurofeedback operates by focusing on individual brain sites. This mechanism measures and feeds back information about a single (monopolar) signal. Neurofeedback training that uses a monopolar amplitude-based approach appeals to the brain to generate greater and more consistent amplitudes at selected frequencies. This approach generally disregards phase, because it addresses brain activity at selected sites.

Phase training however, involves training the phase relationship between two sites in order to promote *phase differences*. This procedure trains the brain's ability to meet challenges, become more flexible, and problem solve automatically and without conscious reasoning. This is because the timing relationship between different brain sites is the most critical variable when it comes to the brain's internal communication in connection with state management.

Here's how it works:

Electrodes are placed at two scalp sites during each training period, and the rewards (moments when the video game progresses) are set to occur when the *two sites show phase differences in activity*. Let's look at this mathematically and then relate it to improvements in brain activity and daily life.

Signals from two sites are said to be *in phase* when their amplitudes reach peak (+1) and nadir (-1) simultaneously. They are *out of phase* when one signal approaches +1 and the other approaches -1 simultaneously. (When two signals are perfectly in phase, they are said to be *synchronous*.) As we train by playing the video game, our brain is intermittently rewarded for "figuring out" how to make the frequency cycles from each site occur at slightly different times. ("You" think you are piloting a spaceship on the screen, while your brain is in the control room, working furiously to figure out the timing codes to keep things moving.) In phase-based training, the reward is not based on the amplitude, but rather on the timing differences between when each of the two signals reaches that amplitude. Mathematically, the rewards occur when the differences become greater (i.e., move away from zero toward an absolute value of one, either positive or negative).

Think of this as similar to teaching instrumentalists in an orchestra to play different notes at the same time (or teaching your hands to play different notes on the piano at staggered time intervals). The effects of this kind of flexibility are astounding and infinite. When you can master playing different notes in varying combinations of time synchrony, you are becoming a master, perhaps eventually a virtuoso.

Taking the musical analogy a step further, phase training is like teaching the brain to sing in harmony, in choral rounds, and in synchrony, as needed. Phase training tunes and trains the brain modules to coordinate among themselves and to communicate with the outside world like a practiced and well-timed group of musicians. You may be familiar with singing in staggered choral rounds. Remember the song, "Row, Row, Row Your Boat"? When two groups sing it together, they are in phase, and the timing code looks like this:

Group 1

| *Row, row, row your boat* | *Gently down the stream* | *Merrily, merrily, merrily, merrily,* | *Life is but a dream.* |

Group 2

| *Row, row, row your boat* | *Gently down the stream* | *Merrily, merrily, merrily, merrily,* | *Life is but a dream.* |

However, when they sing in choral rounds, they are out of phase, and it looks like this:

Group 1

Row, row, row your boat	Gently down the stream	Merrily, merrily, merrily, merrily,	Life is but a dream.

Group 2

Merrily, merrily, merrily, merrily,	Life is but a dream.	Row, row, row your boat	Gently down the stream

Notice that singing in rounds and transitioning back to unison requires careful attention, as well as the ability to focus narrowly and then expand that focus to incorporate the context, sequence, and timing. In order to do this properly, you must be able to shift as necessary. This is a complex task, yet most elementary school students are able to do it (provided that their brains are functioning well). When our brain can shift time codes and integrate and adapt different timing mechanisms, we can pay attention, screen out distractions, maintain continuity, sift and shift to accommodate salient details, and follow a task through to its conclusion.

Does this sound like something you want to be able to do better and more consistently? Neurofeedback—and phase training in particular—will help you far along that path.

When your brain learns to differentiate its timing mechanisms (which is what phase training conditions it to do), you progressively achieve the following:

- Freedom from symptoms
- Improved performance and efficiency
- Better, quicker accessibility to appropriate responses
- Faster recovery from fatigue and stress
- More endurance
- Greatly enhanced flexibility
- Less vulnerability to overreactions

- Better self-regulation and self-control
- Enhanced creativity
- Better concentration
- Improved perception and coordination
- Better sensitivity to people
- Reduced carelessness
- Less defensiveness, hypervigilance, or fight/flight mode
- Increased empathy, compassion, contentment
- Reduced tendency to become overwhelmed or absorbed by pain
- Improved ability to filter distractions, focus sharply, and multitask

The general consensus in the field of neurofeedback is that these results are achieved with most populations using any of the methodologies described. The collective success rates reported by neurotherapists worldwide are approximately (and conservatively) 80 percent. Such success notwithstanding, the advent of *infra-low frequency* (ILF) reward-based training has sped up the progress for most people and has advanced the success level and quality of life impact upon especially difficult populations and conditions: autism, bipolar disorder, seizures, migraines, and addictions.

How Low Can You Go?

For decades, EEG neurofeedback utilized the training of brainwaves in the frequency ranges (bandwidths) recognized to incorporate common waking and sleeping neurophysiology. Technically, this refers to the frequency range between 1 Hz and approximately 60 Hz (cycles per second). Actually, the functional range for training has been more stringently between 1–30 Hz, and the focus of reward and inhibition has typically been between 3–22 Hz.

Researchers and clinicians at the Brian Othmer Foundation (www. EEGinfo.com) have pioneered and developed new software and treatment training protocols that utilize *infra-low frequencies* (ILF). These are brainwave frequencies below 1.0 Hz. Training with these protocols may concern itself with brain activity as low as .00001 Hz, training phase relationships in the same manner described above. The effects of these ILF training protocols are powerful and rather rapid. The results for many people—including people with previously intractable conditions—have often been significant.

From a neurobiological and electrophysiological perspective, brainwave signals below 1 Hz represent biological phenomena that are fundamental to self-regulation, but occur well beneath any radar of consciousness. Whereas frequency bandwidths in the 5–20 Hz range are associated with mental activities anywhere from creative imagining to debating, studying, planning, and calculation; frequencies below 0.1 Hz are associated with longer-term biological encoding.

At the extremely low frequencies, we are most likely paying selective attention to those brain mechanisms involved in organizing our persistent states. These ILFs relate to cycles of mood and of the physiology correlated with mood, such as the state of the autonomic nervous system. They also relate to issues of maturation and aging and the recording and encoding of primitive memories by brain substructures. These encodings often carry information about traumatic events the brain has experienced throughout a person's lifetime.

From a metaphorical standpoint, one might compare the relationships and continuum of traditional brainwave frequencies and infra-low brainwave frequencies with the life-forms on land and beneath the surface of the sea. Yes, there is a vast and only partially explored world down there, teeming with life energy and the potential to teach and nourish us. We mostly concern ourselves with the visible and tangible phenomena that we can access and relate to. In perspective however, what is above sea level is quite literally the tip of the iceberg. This is also true with the new frontier of infra-low brainwave frequencies.

By training at these ILFs, the brain can nonverbally and subconsciously "figure out" how to meet self-regulation challenges that affect conscious perceptions, experiences, and behavior. ILF neurofeedback training has opened a new world of healing and growth possibilities for populations ranging from the severely impaired to high-functioning individuals in all walks of life who want to break through barriers and perform at the top of their capacities.[16]

Not surprisingly, the empirical findings with regard to ILF training find support in the latest research in the neurosciences, where brain-imaging studies are revealing the existence of distinct, well-organized "resting states," to which the brain returns after mastering a challenge. The quality of organization of our resting state networks determines how well we function. Neurofeedback applied in the ILF ranges seems to most effectively challenge the brain to organize its resting state networks.

Mastering Anxiety and Its Cohorts

With this understanding of the neurophysiological foundation of anxiety, we have more information and resources for overcoming anxiety.

Training one's brain will go a very long way toward establishing better self-control, inner harmony and regulation, and put a person more comfortably in the driver's seat for living with and mastering their emotions.

---

16. The field is indebted to Siegfried Othmer, Sue Othmer, and Kurt Othmer for their continuing brilliance, dedication, and perseverance in bringing neurofeedback innovations to the world.

PART III

PERSPECTIVES: ELIMINATE, OVERCOME, ENDURE

CHAPTER 13

Keep Anxiety Away

Throughout this book, I have stressed the pervasiveness of anxiety and its pernicious effects, and I've described various ways of dealing with it. In reviewing the manifestations of anxiety and related disorders and symptoms, as well as the associated spectrum of worry, trauma, negative thinking, and obsessive intrusive thoughts and rumination, I have shared, and sometimes criticized, the conventional (and less-than-adequate) interventions typically advocated and applied to the treatment of anxiety. In proposing better solutions, I have particularly endorsed two current and effective treatments for anxiety and many other forms of mental and emotional distress: Thought Field Therapy (TFT) and EEG neurofeedback. Whether you are encouraged, excited, hopeful, skeptical, or a combination thereof about the potential for overcoming the internal obstacles that may have diminished the well-being and quality of your life or of someone you care for, I recommend each of these methods for vanquishing anxiety and making it stay away.

Understanding that anxiety, to varying degrees, is a product of our biological makeup and the nervous system's way of protecting us and gearing us up and down for the different demands we face, it is natural to wonder if any treatments can truly reduce and/or eliminate anxiety. We must consider the comprehensiveness and endurance that any intervention may promise and deliver.

To What Extent Can We Make Anxiety Go Away?

The anxiety family of worries, fears, restimulations, and traumatic underpinnings creep up and intrude on us as a result of many triggers and vulnerabilities, reminding us with forceful persistence that all is not okay. Many sufferers use medications, intoxicants, behavior responses, reassurance, and various therapies in an attempt to subdue the beast, or at least corral it until it escapes and reemerges. Considering the repetitive intercession that anxiety seems to require—daily medication, habitual intoxication, therapy *ad nauseam*—it may sound fantastic or unrealistic to imagine outcomes that actually get rid of anxiety, and to then feel confident that anxiety will actually stay away.

Bear in mind that anxiety is biologically endemic and serves some necessary and useful purposes (danger alert, protection, carefulness, conscience), the continuum of anxiety blurs between native utility and excessive dysfunction. Anxiety and its cohorts are not unitary, nor an all-or-nothing dimension. Splinters and tapeworms can be removed in entirety; polyps can be excavated, and even bullets can often be wholly taken out. Cancerous tumors and invasions can be eradicated. With cancer, we speak of "remission," hedging bets cautiously against its resurgence, and measuring cure in increments of benign years and probabilities.

Anxiety is different in that some of it is necessary and healthy. For instance, the arousal curve describes a parabola of motivation where low arousal correlates with low motivation and lethargy, and over-arousal predicts panic, avoidance, and even paralysis. A surplus or inappropriate recurrence of anxiety borders on disabling.

Other biological features and habits detour into disorders. Variations and problems with eating, sleeping, movement, and exercise often result in injury, disease, excess, or plain long-term misery. Yet we cannot eliminate these functions just because they become problematic. As the saying advises, "Don't throw the baby out with the bath water."

In wanting to preserve the natural biological utility of anxiety while preventing it from taking over, where do we draw lines and what should our expectations be?

Is It Just the Way You Are?

Sad to say, most of the historical and conventional thinking—largely propounded and reinforced by professionals—is that some people simply have *anxious personalities*. This construct is a sweeping and pejorative generalization that goes far beyond the accepted view that genetic constituents predispose us to probabilities of developing diseases and afflictions. Just as heart disease, diabetes, and allergies, anxiety, depression, and other mental problems can run in families, some people are more vulnerable and predisposed to those afflictions. However, such biological underpinnings are a far cry from labeling people with recalcitrant anxiety as *anxious personalities.*

We don't label people with migraines or seizures as "migraine or seizure personalities?" Is there such a thing as a "cancer personality?"

For many people, anxieties are persistent afflictions that respond minimally to traditional therapies and recur with pernicious resilience despite repeated interventions. This debilitation not only afflicts sufferers, but it frustrates mental health professionals. The attitude of "It's just the way they are: they have anxious personalities" is a poor professional reaction and foreclosure to the insufficiency of our field to effectively address this problem. Rather than admit failure, professional convention often blames the patient. As a seasoned therapist told me, "I work with the clay I am given."

Buried in the seeming wisdom of facing limits is the surprising truth in the allegory that "the emperor wears no clothes." That the majority subscribes to a myth of pretension does not confirm its truth!

Using EEG neurofeedback and TFT, my colleagues and I have shown time and again with thousands of patients that people who have struggled with anxiety for decades—even those who have self-identified and resigned themselves to being hapless and hopeless worriers—have turned the corner and subdued their anxieties to the point where their lives are transformed!

How Long Does It Last?

To clearly address the endurance of results, I must invoke some perspective. My practice of Voice Technology has a sustained 97 percent success rate over several decades. By success I mean that my patients' presenting symptoms were *completely eliminated, typically within fifteen minutes.* I often video and audio record my sessions, and patients have documented their changes in their own writing. I have thousands of such records as evidence. Though these results are astounding, they are routine. This treatment works faster than aspirin or Ativan!

When confronted with this incontrovertible evidence, patients and skeptics alike ask, "How long does it last?"

The answers are complicated, varied, but factual. In my clinical experience, about 80 percent of Voice Technology TFT treatments have had enduring results. To qualify: the elimination of the symptoms treated continued for a period of time, ranging from days to indefinitely. Certain categories of problems have notably long endurance. Encapsulated traumas (specific to a discrete event, such as an assault or rape) and phobias, in particular, usually stay away after one or several treatments. Each individual treatment eliminates the symptoms, however some phobias and traumas may contain multiple thought fields that are not uncovered or addressed in the first treatment.

Recurrent anxieties in chronically anxious or pervasively disturbed patients need multiple treatments. Each successive application chips away at the perturbed thought fields and produces more resilient and lasting results. The 20 percent whose results are recalcitrant comprise a combination of multiple traumas, complex thought fields, and toxins that cause reversals and the recurrence of symptoms that were successfully treated.

That a few minutes of treatment can *completely eliminate* symptoms that have persisted and resisted for years is nothing sort of remarkable. As people's perceptions change over time, they may develop higher standards and expectations as a result of the treatment successes already experienced.

Reversals and Toxins

When treatment is conducted successfully with TFT (as in the vast majority of treatments), the perturbations in the thought field are deactivated, rendering a disconnection between the disturbing emotions and thoughts associated with them. Thus, the symptoms are rapidly and completely eliminated. The original perturbed code that caused the problem is still there, but it is essentially "unindexed" or separated from the problematic connection. (Think of a disconnected phone service; the original number is on record, but it is not active.)

Though most TFT treatments last when the relevant thought fields have been treated, the treated symptoms return in instances of recurrence due to "psychological reversal." As discussed previously, psychological reversals can interfere with treatment progress unless corrected, because they reactivate the original causative code connecting the perturbed thought field with its resultant negative emotion, which causes the symptoms to return. Such reversals may be induced by new traumas, injuries, or illnesses that assault the protective strength of resilience. However, the occurrence of such events is unlikely and not necessarily predictive of reversal affecting the successfully treated problem. The majority of reversals causing recurrence are the result of *toxins*, known as an *individual energy toxin* (IET).

Toxins are a critically important issue for many, especially those enmeshed in negative addictive cycles, complex traumas or abuse, and longstanding mental illness or maladjustment. Toxins, the substances that cause a psychological reversal and may block or reverse the effects of successful treatment, typically include various foods, toiletries, aromas, and supplements that are toxic to a percentage of people. For many, the sustained positive effects of treatments and better health require the identification of and abstention from toxins. Toxins can be identified through basic level diagnosis by trained practitioners, Voice technology (VT) is most expedient in the identification of toxins that may cause psychological reversals and interfere with treatment.

Toxins can often induce a psychological reversal that has the effect of "undoing" or reversing a previously successful treatment and also of interfering or blocking the progress of an incipient treatment.

Aside from its impact upon TFT treatments, the effect of psychological reversal is a major factor in many other treatment methods and can undermine desired goal-oriented motivational states.

As creatures of habit, we like to do what we do, and eat what we want to eat. No one likes to be told that preferred foods are causing problems. Moreover, though we are familiar with admonitions about "healthy" eating, the idea that some "nourishing" (but toxic) foods are bad for us goes against the grain and common sense. However, nature does not always conform to our notions, and it behooves us to adapt to reality and evidence. Many people become wise to the information that certain foods are not good for them. Common offenders like dairy, nuts, etc., cause physiological distress such as gastric problems or headaches in many.

Grains and spices in particular are problematic for millions, even in the absence of medically diagnosed allergies. There is a sound evolutionary basis for this. Animals can escape predators through mobility. Plants cannot run away. Thus, many plants develop chemical protection that dissuades predators. The spillover from this evolutionary guard can also affect humans. Many people are highly sensitive to certain grains. While these foods may not make them physically sick, the can act as toxins, causing psychological reversal that makes symptoms recur. This deeper level of food sensitivity is unfamiliar to most people, but it is empirically valid.

Many times I have tested patients by voice and determined things they are eating or self-care products they use that cause such reversals. After the reversals are corrected and treatment is readministered, the treatments last—if the person abstains from the offending toxins. Though it is a significant inconvenience to abstain from desired foods, the verifiable results are well worth the sacrifice.

Neurofeedback's Enduring Effects

Addressing anxiety and other forms of mental distress reveals sharp contrasts between conventional treatment methods such as medication (requiring daily dosages), talk therapy (usually requiring many visits over years), and the use of the powerful technological treatments of TFT and neurofeedback.

TFT treatments are powerful, rapid, and usually enduring. However, they do not train the brain and nervous system to build self-regulation, flexibility, and resilience. For these components of health, neurofeedback provides a comprehensive and lasting solution.

The operation and effects of neurofeedback are nonlogical (actually *neurological*). Modality notwithstanding, most patients begin to accept its validity when they examine research, hear reports, and experience the results. Yet the questions surface: *How long will it last? Do I need to do this indefinitely? What if my problem comes back?*

That the positive results of neurofeedback are enduring has been the collective experience of myself, many colleagues, and thousands of patients. People tend to maintain their gains from treatment long afterward. As in other areas of life, events such as injury, illness, trauma, and other adverse setbacks can make people regress. An important context is how stable and adjusted the person is and/or has been for some period of time. A distressing medical diagnosis, loss of a job or loved one, or other adversities can lower the threshold for the return of symptoms. In almost all cases however, neurofeedback builds robustness that limits the extent of regression and allows the person subsequent recovery that is quicker and fuller.

Though the treatment effects are enduring and people usually maintain the gains they've achieved, there are reasons to continue or come back for more neurofeedback training. Once past their overwhelming distress, many people want to tackle other challenges, such as peak performance for some skill, hobby, spiritual, business, or athletic pursuit. They may want to use neurofeedback as an adjunct to improve relationships and build better emotional stability, empathy, and confidence. Neurofeedback facilitates and augments family therapy and marriage counseling, because it trains the individuals involved to control their emotions calmly and listen more objectively and attentively.

People with developmental disabilities (such as autism and learning disorders) need more training, though they also tend to maintain their gains even when they stop treatment. Degenerative conditions (e.g., dementia, multiple sclerosis, Parkinson's, etc.) that respond well to neurofeedback typically need some degree of further treatment.

Addictions take longer, as the underlying pathologies emerge once the addictive urge and habit is brought under control. For perspective, compare months of neurofeedback treatment with inpatient rehab, daily intensive outpatient program (IOP), sober living arrangements, and years of therapy—all costing tens or hundreds of thousands of dollars. Relapse is common.

Neurofeedback helps people resume and advance the gains they made without starting from square one.

Other Elements of Keeping Anxiety Away

TFT and neurofeedback are extremely effective at vanquishing anxiety. Each works individually and often has a combined synergistic effect, building flexibility and resilience, and offering lasting effects. Along with some professional guidance, each of these methods can be self-practiced.

For self-administered TFT, the Appendix provides a number of algorithms that are useful for specific problems and negative emotional states, such as anxiety, cravings, depression, and so forth. This appendix also includes some tips and techniques I have found successful in treating many people and problems over the years. An expedient tool for self-treatment is found in a video series I developed, accessible on my website.

Some neurofeedback practitioners such as myself offer programs for home training, whereby clients can lease or purchase equipment and train remotely under clinical supervision. This arrangement offers convenience and facilitates more training. However, those considering this option should be advised not to undertake starting it without the supervision of an experienced neurofeedback professional. Supervised remote training usually begins with in-office neurofeedback to establish and oversee the right protocols and trends in progress and response to treatment. Using the right equipment is essential. Be wary of the multitude of devices available for low cost on the internet.

Along with effective treatments, I recommend adopting and practicing lifestyle habits that keep anxiety from creeping back and taking over.

Adequate rest and sleep

Consistent and appropriate sleep is indispensable for health and good brain functioning. Yet tens of millions of people struggle with sleep. Though not a panacea, neurofeedback is one of the best solutions for resetting the brain's sleep/wake rhythms. Good sleep hygiene is also critical, most notably establishing routines and consistency as much as possible. We need to make our body our servants. As we establish routines and habits, our body and brain will eventually cooperate and make the process easier. Going to bed at around the same time nightly is most helpful. If work or other schedules permit, go to bed early and wake up early. This is the natural evolutionary design. Though some may have to work graveyard shifts, no one must stay up through the wee hours playing video games.

As well as regular good sleep, we must develop and make time for recharging our biological and psychological batteries through recreation and relaxation. *All work and no play makes for dullness and stress. Equally, stress makes for dullness and lack of motivation for work or play.* It may seem peculiar, but we have to learn and practice having fun and relaxation. There's no shame in that.

Refrain from alcohol and recreational intoxicants

Those hooked on drinking or use of intoxicants are well aware that these substances temporarily reduce anxiety and provide escape and relief from stress. Also true, though less obvious, substance use has a rebound effect when it wears off. Unfortunately, the anxiety returns because what caused it was not addressed—and the substances themselves incite the brain to become more dysregulated and prone to anxiety.

Drinking alcohol has sedating effects that induce sleep. In addition to developing dependency, the drinker tends to awaken and have more difficulty falling back asleep once alcohol metabolizes. This is also the case with many prescribed sleep medications.

Cannabis is popular for in relieving anxiety and making people "chill." However, it has known damaging effects on brain function, including reductions in cognitive functions, motivation, and the brain's natural ability to regulate fight-or-flight mechanisms and internal state shifts.

Ironically, the substances used to quell anxiety end up magnifying its recurrence. This is disheartening, but not surprising. The brain needs to modulate effectively on its own. If we douse our bloodstream with a quick fix of sugar, we feel better temporarily. But then we pay the piper as blood sugar plummets, needless calories are quickly expended, we need repeated fixes, and eventually develop food addictions and added health problems.

Diet and nutrition

I cannot overemphasize how important proper nutrition and eating habits are to keeping anxiety at bay. I am not the *food police*; nor am I a nutritional expert. I have learned scientifically as well as vicariously while helping patients, and also with my own struggles how food affects people emotionally as well as physically.

Hunger and health depend pivotally on the management of blood sugar. Our bodies are fine-tuned to digest foods and convert nutrients to energy. A precarious balance exists between releasing sugar into the bloodstream and counteracting it with insulin. Too little sugar in the system results in hypoglycemia, and feeling weak and shaky. Too much sugar overloads the organs and causes a cyclical rebound effect of a temporary energetic sugar high, followed by a rebound or "crash" in which the body craves more sugar quickly. On this uncomfortable and unhealthy rollercoaster is where most Americans spend their days and appetites. Over time, too much blood sugar causes the body to become insulin resistant, a condition in which the insulin produced by the pancreas is insufficient to counteract and balance blood sugar. Eventually, this results in diabetes.

Processed foods, and especially simple carbohydrates (which the body converts to sugar), provide quicker fuel; but they burn quickly, leaving us hungry and craving more. Complex carbs (such as those found in legumes, vegetables, and some fruits) break down more slowly, as do proteins. Three ounces of fish or chicken or beans is much more satisfying and energy producing than three ounces of chips or bread.

Keeping blood sugar under control has a direct positive impact on minimizing anxiety, impulsivity, cravings, satiety, and self-regulation. Discovering foods that disagree is also pivotal to keeping calm and even-tempered.

Social interaction

Anxiety tends to inhibit social interaction or at least render it more stressful. People have energy fields, and our energy "auras" and projections influence each other. Ironically, excess anxiety deters social interaction and makes sufferers avoidant, even though social interaction is a great tool to drive down anxiety. This chicken-and-egg cycle between people provoking anxiety, thereby increasing avoidance, and people providing necessary "human" nourishment must be resolved to create happiness and satisfaction.

It's similar to the anxiety-addiction cycle, where withdrawal incurs anxiety and cravings, but indulgent relief just feeds and strengthens the addiction.

Proper treatments lower anxiety and pave the way for the bonding and strengthening of social ties that should and can be quite rewarding.

Curiosity, intellectual stimulation, art, music, romance, passion

When we are anxious, it's hard to focus, relax, and experience pleasure. Anxiety disengages the motivation and energy to participate. However, engaging our mind with stimulating, fascinating, awe-inspiring, or emotionally titillating experiences promotes neurological reward and emotional satisfaction.

Natural experiences that foster increased "pleasure neurotransmitters" take advantage of the incompatibility between anxiety and good pleasure.

As my father taught me with his pranks long ago, you can't chew a mouthful of peanut butter and crackers and whistle simultaneously.

Prayer

Are you someone who desires to break free from rules? Do you like to give your opinion or complain? Do you appreciate someone who truly listens and seek such an audience? Is your life filled with stress and strife?

Personal prayer appeals to all of these needs. No rules, no necessary format: prayer is free, constant, and gives unbound access to our Creator. God listens (doesn't always answer how and when we want though), doesn't judge our prayers, and most of all, *cares!*

Prayer allows us to blatantly be ourselves and explore our feelings—those we accept as well as those that are troubling. Prayer invites us to express ourselves without fear, embarrassment, or recriminations. Prayer is always available, and God always listens. Prayer gets better with practice. Nothing is a more natural, fulfilling, and effective way to calm anxiety than prayer.

Managing Versus Eliminating Anxiety

Circling back a bit, I offer my thoughts about the difference between getting rid of anxiety and managing anxiety.

As mentioned previously, most conventional thinking, largely propounded and reinforced by professionals, is that some people simply have *anxious personalities*. In light of this "convenient" rationalization (deduced from the failure of most traditional therapies in getting rid of anxiety on an enduring basis), the standard professional view is that the most realistic achievable outcome is to help patients *manage* their anxiety. I believe this is a low and inadequate standard. We may manage employees or manage our in-laws (hopefully not to get rid of them). We manage budgets or traffic, etc. If we have a tapeworm, do we manage it and learn to live with it? Certainly not—we get rid of it!

My view (formed from experience and practice) about anxiety is that most of it (in excess) can be eliminated on an enduring basis. The most grievous and disruptive aspects and manifestations of anxiety—traumas, panic attacks, addictions, phobias, insomnia—are very amenable and responsive to TFT and neurofeedback.

Living with anxiety (or tapeworms) is unnecessary, and tolerating the afflictions of anxiety and its cohorts can be treated successfully enough that the overbearing and constant anxieties—the shackles of living with anxiety—are truly eliminated.

We can take charge of our body and mind to a greater extent than our suffering and vulnerabilities would coerce us to fear and believe. With a combination of modern, effective, and appropriate professional treatment, attention and diligence to self-care and healthy lifestyles, and the inclusion of self-treatments, the damaging influences of anxiety can be subdued, eliminated, and kept away.

CHAPTER 14

Expectations, Reality, and Idealized Life

Yet man is born to trouble as surely as sparks fly upward. (Job 5:7)

But godliness with contentment is great gain. (1 Timothy 6:6)

I've heard it said that nothing is certain except death and taxes. Even with our capitulation to our government dues, and eventually to nature, hope springs as long as we can muster it—if not eternal!

Despite adversity, perhaps because of it, we look to the future with much desire and some expectations that life will improve. We want to believe that better things lie ahead, and we rely on promises from those we trust to make our hopes and expectations come true.

To diminish our anxiety and get out from under its relentless pressure, we must find ways to match and reconcile what we hope for and expect from the realities concerning what is possible and likely in light of our experiences, our plans for improvement, and the standards we set for meeting our expectations.

In this closing chapter, we take a look at the role of anxiety in life, what we expect regarding overcoming it, the reality of limitations, and what we can realistically do to effect positive change and accept the parts of life that fall short of our idealized desires.

Expectations

An expectation is the belief or anticipation that something will happen or be the case in the future. Expectations represent our pictures, records, and desires of how life is and should be. We all have expectations that are a product of our conscious mind, the conglomeration of our previous learning, our images of things to come, desires for what we want, and beliefs about what is likely to happen. Without expectations, we could hardly plan or build mental models and concepts about the way the world operates. Expectations help us predict, categorize, and simplify, forming a cornerstone of what we know as reality.

At a biological level, expectations propel our survival by guiding behavior toward physical needs and functions. Animals in the wild go where they expect to find food, water, and safety. People generally act in ways we think will bring similar rewards. At a physiological level, our expectations gear our nervous systems to states of arousal necessary or appropriate for anticipated events. At a psychological level, expectations drive our mind's narrative to support our evaluation of experiences and our predictions of what might happen next.

A downside to expectations is that desire, need, or faulty evaluations can drive expectations to the point where our hopes are dashed, beliefs are unrealistic, and disappointments prevail over satisfaction and fulfillment. Expectations are the mediators between reality and desire that help us navigate through the world as it is, toward the world we wish to create. Our expectations are the assessments, plans and schematics, aspirations, and maps of the world and ourself within the world.

Greater and Lesser Expectations

I have frequently observed that people have and form differing expectations based upon what they want and what they get. I describe these differences as greater expectations and lesser expectations. *Greater expectations* indicate results hoped for or desired involving aspirations, ambitions, imagination, wishes, and dreams. *Lesser expectations* refer to the realistically anticipated results that are based upon previous experiences and conditioning and involve predictive validity, accuracy, boundaries, practicality, and directions. Expectations unfold at different levels that mediate the ways that we want things to be (greater expectations) with the ways we have learned through experience that they are likely to play out (lesser expectations).

The difference between our greater expectations and our lesser expectations will usually approximate our resulting satisfactions and disappointments in life. Such differences serve as indicators of the extent to which we are able to reconcile the outcomes we attain with the way we want our life to work, and allows us to reflect on the way we balance reality testing with desire. As we make efforts to rid ourselves of anxieties, fears, worries, and negativity, we must also navigate, accommodate, and reconcile what we expect, hope, and work toward and the results we get.

Greater expectations are inherently prone to inflated impressions. We generally envision the upside, and place a positive spin on what we anticipate. The antidote is to possess a positive attitude coupled with *discernment* that can help us temper pie-in-the-sky optimism and blindsided disappointments. For this, we need lesser expectations, which are inherently more conservative, to modulate the inflated expectations that often (subconsciously) accompany a sense of entitlement, eagerness, and intensely focused desire to attain an objective that might be overlaid with wishful thinking. The gap between greater and lesser expectations will naturally shrink as the application of TFT and neurofeedback promotes greater improvements in resolving anxiety.

When Expectations Are Not Fulfilled

We will all be disappointed and unfulfilled many times along our life journey. Anxiety and other negative emotions easily infiltrate our reactions to dashed expectations and unrequited hopes. Whether satisfied by progress in defeating anxiety, or frustrated that anxiety still maintains some chokehold, we must come to terms with the differences between what we strive for and what we get. How we do this forms our attitude, future expectations, motivation and actions, and the ways we relate to and affect others.

Resolving discrepancies between greater expectations and lesser expectations is a working model for living life on its own terms—the life practice of *reconciling* feelings and experiences that don't match.

Assessing Reality and Accepting Limits

Throughout this book, I have endeavored to convey that the realization of higher expectations regarding the treatment of anxiety is achievable through modern treatments that far surpass the traditional interventions and forecasts. Notwithstanding the evidence-based and empirical victories brought about through these methods, many people remain constrained by the grip of anxiety, fear, worry, and negative thinking.

How then, can they reconcile the differences?

In health and medicine, as in other domains, nothing is 100 percent. This is an observable reality supported by statistical facts. Medicines have side effects, and they don't work the same for every person. Engineers use a language of *mean time between failures* (MTBF) to describe and predict the durability of products. Statistics on divorce, disease, and natural and social calamities remind us of the precarious vulnerability and fragility of safety and security.

In reviewing conventional views and treatments of anxiety, I have assailed the limitations and prevailing attitudes about the manner and extent of relieving anxiety and other negative emotions. Can overbearing anxiety be vanquished? Will relief last? How realistic are hopes and positive expectations—especially among those whose very problem centers around negativity?!

In light of the abundant evidence attesting to the millions who have overcome anxiety, it is reasonable and demonstrable that high expectations are appropriate and sustained. Yet even the best treatments will work better for some than others. Many will be transformed, while others will attain modest benefit or remain unchanged.

My stand is clear: the limiting and resigned conventional view that managing anxiety is the best we can do falls far short of professional obligation, science, and the success of present and emerging treatments. Concurrently, we must acknowledge the reality that a percentage of people are born with, develop, and revert to a high-strung or cautious, negative, and perfectionistic temperament that seems resistant and determined to cling to the downside of life. These individuals make it hard on themselves and difficult for others. But we cannot and should not simply blame them or dismiss their troubles critically as self-inflicted. We owe them more and better, even if they push back or do not respond well.

We owe them encouragement and care, even if they are feisty, defensive, skeptical, or denigrating. With suffering or dying patients, we don't punish, neglect, or treat them with harshness or contempt. We are gentle and offer nurturing, sympathy, and encouragement, as well as the best treatment relief at our disposal.

Along with life's joys and advantages, there are plenty of reasons to worry. Some people develop a lifestyle of worrying and spreading their negativity. We still owe them compassion, patience, and a lighted path away from recalcitrance, guilt, and despair, along with the freedom to make their own choices. Despite their pushback and cynicism, the worrywarts of the world appreciate these efforts and will make what progress they can. For the downtrodden, injured, traumatized, and defeated, even tiny steps and rewards can be savored.

How Much Is Good Enough?

In striving for goal attainment—including the reduction of pain and adversity—aiming high and falling short can be profitable. Of course, we need to temper hopes with realistic evidence (and reconcile greater and lesser expectations). When deficiencies are burdensome, small gains can often liberate the "tires from being stuck in the rut" and propel forward movement and freedom.

Consider some examples: Over the course of my career as a psychologist, I've evaluated thousands of people, including many students with learning disabilities. Among the spectrum of learning disorders, deficits can occur in some particular areas of functioning while other cognitive functions are much higher. For example, many students have delays or deficits in eye-hand coordination or visual motor skills. These individuals may show test results at the sixth percentile or lower. In such a profile, we can predict that the student will have great difficulty copying, taking notes, and writing while listening. These deficits clearly decrease academic performance and induce great frustration for the student.

Though the specific learning disability described may persist for years, I've found that remediation to improve visual motor skills even *somewhat* usually makes a *significant* difference in the student's performance and ability to succeed with the curriculum. Raising visual motor performance to the ninth percentile seems to make a "just-good-enough difference" that results in better learning and adjustment, and more motivation.

A similar "just-good-enough difference" can occur with weight loss. Someone may be significantly overweight, yet losing just five to ten pounds can make a huge difference in morale and motivation, the fit of clothing, and blood pressure.

Doing the Best We Can, and Better

Speaking of weight loss, consider this: after the Reverend Al Sharpton lost 175 pounds, he said, "I lost more weight than I weigh now." Fantastic! (I've lost 102 pounds since my heaviest—not like Sharpton, but still a significant accomplishment.) Reverend Sharpton's experience can serve as a metaphor for getting rid of anxiety: if you've lost more fear, anxiety, and worry than you now have, that great accomplishment and probably correlates with greater contentment.

Learning and practicing perseverance is crucial in many areas of life, and it especially bears fruit in dealing with anxiety. Getting back up when you fall eventually develops resilience and teaches that failures, false starts, and successive approximations (psychological jargon for small successful increments and progressive steps) are necessary parts of attaining mastery.

To discover that we can face fears, conquer many of them, and live peaceably with other intrusions is transforming. I'm not suggesting that one ignore overwhelming panic, paralyzing phobias, or the stifling effects of trauma. But I assure you that most of these can be eliminated or at least greatly lessened. The reality exists that, for some people, stamping out fear and worry entirely remains elusive. Reducing some or most of the anxiety may be sufficient to allow much greater freedom and functioning while promoting tolerance of the remaining problem. It's a matter of critical thresholds and some noticeable differences (as in the above examples) that lift us above defeating levels of dysfunction.

As we make progress and recognize increases in strength, recovery, and tolerance, small gains turn into larger practical gains that are meaningful, satisfying, motivating, and which facilitate more reinforcement.

A Bad Day

Everyone has "bad" days. My turn came when several events cascaded to the point where I was tempted to attribute my bad luck to a negative horoscope.

In the morning, a pipe burst and flooded my garage. After dealing with that emergency as best I could for the interim, I decided to exercise to relieve stress. I went to the gym, where I worked out and swam for ninety minutes. Upon returning to my locker, I discovered that someone had broken in and stolen my credit cards. As if this weren't enough, my cellphone stopped working.

After several hours of trying to repair this emergency (borrowing phones, camping out in the Apple Store, calling my carrier), it turned out that my service had been deactivated by my carrier for no apparent reason. After I jumped through the hoops of authenticating my identity on borrowed phones (without access to my database or passwords), the provider acknowledged their error and I was eventually able to restore service. By evening, I was flooded with accumulated emails, voicemails, and notifications that someone had tried to fraudulently charge fifty thousand dollars of merchandise on my stolen credit cards!

Was I upset? A little (no understatement here—honestly, just a little.) Anxious? Again, just a little.

Clearly, the day had accumulated traumas. But over time, I have become desensitized and somewhat inured to the frustrations and insults that inevitably come my way, sometimes pummeling me. I've had credit cards hijacked before. I've been robbed. Phone and computer malfunctions are routine (expected, but not specifically predictable).

But through years of physical and mental training, I've become much better able to weather these traumas and "poor me" victimizations without much overarousal or anxiety. Even my indignation at insults and injustices diminishes very rapidly now.

To counteract my frustration, I felt sorry for the criminals who disadvantaged me, as I reminded myself that they are succumbing to an evil path that has predictable consequences, despite my misfortune in the path of their self-destruction. My compassion and prayers extended to the hapless customer service reps who must respond daily to impatient customers like me in the wake of corporate inefficiency and incompetence.

In place of what may have once caused huge anxiety, anger, and self-pity (though I still maintain some reserve), I have developed greater compassion and tolerance, and a steely determination to solve problems. I attribute this to God's help along with a steady adherence to a healthy lifestyle (no alcohol or drugs, careful diet, consistent sleep and exercise, following sane medical advice, and spending most of my time helping others).

Along the way to maturity and spiritual development, my own self-treatment with TFT and neurofeedback has built resilience, a calm and flexible brain, and the wherewithal to withstand and rebound from adversity with more compassion, forgiveness and understanding, as well as less personalization and self-pity when things don't go my way.

Though I don't put stock in astrology, I do subscribe to cosmic and spiritual influence, especially that of the powerful God who watches over and cares so much about me.

Here is my perfect salve for that bad day from Psalm 23. My applications are in [*italics*].

> The Lord is my shepherd, I lack nothing. He makes me lie down in green pastures, he leads me beside quiet waters, he refreshes my soul.
> [*The Lord makes me calm in the face of everything, and he renews me.*]

> He guides me along the right paths for his name's sake.
> [*The Lord shows me what to do to solve problems and cope with adversity, such as the wherewithal to restore my losses.*]

Even though I walk through the darkest valley,
I will fear no evil, for you are with me; your rod and your staff,
they comfort me.
[*God protects me from the powerful forces of evil, preserving me from*
further destruction.]

You prepare a table before me in the presence of my enemies.
[*He provides restoration and supplies my needs (replaces credit cards,*
fixes pipes, restores phone service).]

You anoint my head with oil;
[*God allows me honor by leading me to people who will respect and*
help me (customer service).]

my cup overflows.
[*After a day of setbacks and traumas, I returned to my wife, dog, ma-*
terial comforts, and abundant possessions.]

Surely your goodness and love will follow me all the days of my
life, and I will dwell in the house of the Lord forever.
[*God is always there, and I look forward to the future and expect good*
things because of His promises]

Following the "bad" things that happened on the day I described,
I returned home, my body, mind, and soul feeling good, and I wrote
this poem:

Forces

Weakness, fatigue and gravity
Conspire to be the boss of me.
With due respect for nature's forces,
I train to battle further losses.

Brain and body work together
Building balance and resilience.
Nature takes away in stages,
Formidable as one ages.

I take control nonetheless,
Delighting as small steps progress.
Deliberately directing motion,
Countering the slow erosion.

Though body leans toward entropy,
It can be regulated.
The brain discovers how to be
A system more elated.

Perseverance and acceptance choreograph their dance,
Challenging and learning limits helps the soul advance.
Centrifugal, centripetal, accelerators, brakes,
Nature's forces force the harmony that survival takes.

Beyond the endless carousel revolving pleasure and pain,
A code of living takes the soul to find a higher plane.
Expectations may inflate, fulfillment may then wane.
Remember that contentment with godliness is great gain.

At some point we must learn to live beyond the pursuit of pleasure and its exultation, and the avoidance of pain and its subjugation. We can and should reform our habits, adjust our expectations, and reinvent ourselves to become more ideal in a quite imperfect world. Ideal may be the goal, but real must form the mold.

We tend to be absorbed in the present, influenced by momentary physiology that colludes with fretting about the future and recalling the past. We are driven to strive toward destinations: the next acquisition, circumstance, or achievement that promises to make life better. Ironically, when we get that next thing, we then want something or somewhere else, expecting that fulfilling the newer desires will make us happier and more complete.

Desires, goals, and accomplishments are good. We should be responsible and faithful to our obligations. But we but should also derive more joy and fun from the journey.

Occasionally, I reflect on the Irish Proverb my wise mother used to quote, one that gives me perspective and grace: "I complained that I had no shoes until I met a man who had no feet."

The ideal life may be unattainable, but real life can be better than pretty good.

When younger, I ran six miles daily and could stretch my back by lying on the floor and touching my toes to the floor in back of my head. Presently, I'm a dumpy senior citizen with arthritis and limited mobility. Yet I am much happier now than when I was young. God has graced me with peace and contentment in good times and in bad circumstances. I have gratitude and purpose, accepting adversity, limitations, and moving on, doing the best I can. Each morning I arise, oriented toward and determined to make some people's lives just a little better.

Regardless of how much we overcome anxiety, we will still have misfortunes, worries, preoccupations, and bad events. Our nervous systems are naturally prepared for these, but we should not live in a state of vigilance as the norm.

We can grow and become stronger and more flexible, persevering and tolerating, forgiving and accepting, taking comfort in our efforts and integrity, dedicating ourselves to helping others, and delighting in an all-powerful God who assures us that we will not have to do everything ourselves or go it alone.

Learning to accept limitations, to carry on while overlooking defeat, and clothing ourselves with hope and eagerness, we will attain more comfort in a material world that is not truly home. In bringing our troubles, hopes, and expectations to God, we have an ally whose power and love are awesome and miraculous in helping us face the seemingly insurmountable.

At times, the pain and misfortune recede, and we get a brief taste of bliss: a glimpse, a whiff, a whisper, a caress that blesses and foretells what heaven may be like. Anxiety is no match for that.

Break Free From Settling

In his address, "The Weight of Glory," C. S. Lewis said, "Our Lord finds our desires not too strong, but too weak. We are half-hearted creatures, fooling about with drink and sex and ambition when infinite joy is offered us, like an ignorant child who wants to go on making mud pies in a slum because he cannot imagine what is meant by the offer of a holiday at the sea. *We are far too easily pleased.*"

Lewis's idea about our low expectations and meager predilections extols a view that far more pleasure and joy is available than what we seem willing to settle for. He raises the bar on what expectations and outlook should be, based on what God wants and offers us. This lofty view stands in sharp contrast to the frustration and disappointment many feel when expectations are not met and hopes are dashed.

Consumed by the efforts of keeping fight-or-flight at bay and keeping our mind from sliding off the cliff of security and comfort, we often foreclose opportunities to experience peace and contentment and bask in the love and rest that God promises and provides: not only relief, but presence; not escape, but guidance and sustenance.

We do not need to allow ourselves to become isolated, prisoners of fear who are hoodwinked by those distressing arousal signals from the nervous system that alert and protect us. We need not fester in the self-absorption and messiness of mud pies. We have wonderful opportunities that reside within our very nature, brain, and spirit—to take advantage of the seashore invitation, leave the mud pies behind, and renew ourselves in the fresh air of freedom.

Wouldn't you agree and join in such pursuit?

Cast all your anxiety on him because he cares for you. (1 Peter 5:7)

I know what it is to be in need and I know what it is to have plenty.
I have learned the secret of being content in any and every situation,
whether well fed or hungry, whether living in plenty or in want. I
can do all things through him who gives me strength. (Philippians
4:12–13)

Thought Field Therapy (TFT) Algorithms for Self-Healing

The tapping sequences listed in this appendix are *algorithms*—that is, they are recipes that are based on the distillation of many successful treatments that have eliminated negative emotions in others.

Read and familiarize yourself with the material in Chapter 11 before administering the tapping sequences.

Refer to the diagrams to locate the appropriate tapping points.

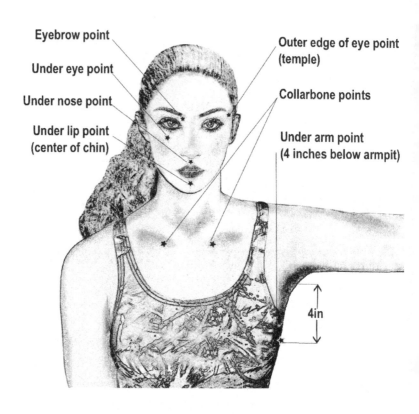

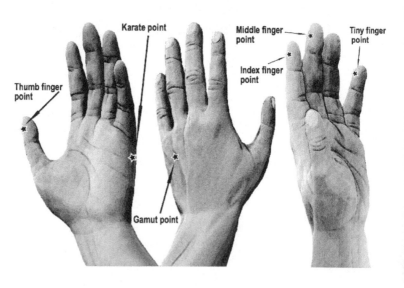

Please note that when you read the following instructions, you may initially feel tentative and/or intimidated by the described procedures. In fact, these procedures are actually very easy to apply. It just takes a bit of practice to get the hang of them. Put any apprehensions you may have on hold and simply follow step-by-step, easy-to understand and easy-to-use procedures. Mastering these methods can be life-altering.

Before you begin each treatment, rate your discomfort or negative feeling about the particular issue you want to treat on a scale of 1 through 10, with 1 meaning that you have none of the symptom whatsoever at present and 10 meaning that the symptom is as bad as it can be for you.

General Guidelines

1. You can use either hand to tap, as well as either side of your body.

2. You can tap with slight pressure—firmly, lightly, and quickly.

3. For the major holon sequences (a holon sequence is a series of meridian tapping points—see below), tap fifteen times on each point.

4. When tapping on the karate point (side of the hand) or under the nose, tap fifteen times.

5. When the gamut point (see diagram) is used as a tapping point in a major holon sequence, it will be designated as "G50"—this means tap it fifty times.

6. When doing the nine-gamut sequence, tap persistently in the gamut point as you do the eye movements and humming and counting.

7. While doing the nine-gamut sequence, breathe naturally and deeply, and keep your head still (move only your eyes).

Administering the TFT Algorithms

1. Make the appropriate statements out loud (See below)
2. Tap a major holon sequence (the specific order of tapping points listed)
3. Then, do the nine-gamut sequence
4. Then tap again the major holon sequence. Essentially, you sandwich a nine-gamut sequence in between repetitions of the major holon sequence for each statement:

"I want to be over . . . (the specific symptom or negative emotion)."
"I want to be *completely* over . . . (the specific symptom or negative emotion)."
"I *will be completely* over . . . (the specific symptom or negative emotion)."

Applying the Nine-Gamut Treatment Sequence

The nine-gamut treatment will result in your distress or negative emotion being reduced even further. Continue to think of your distress or negative emotion and tap solidly (with two fingers) the gamut point on the back of your hand (See diagram). It is located behind and between the little finger knuckle and the ring finger knuckle on the back of your hand. It doesn't matter which hand you use, but many prefer to tap with the dominant hand on the back of the nondominant hand. Keep your head straight with your nose pointed ahead while you do the nine-gamut treatment. Tap about five times for each one of the nine gamut positions while you continue to think of your distress or negative emotion throughout the whole series:

While tapping gamut point on back of hand, do the following:

1. Close your eyes.
2. Open your eyes.
3. Point your eyes way down and way over to the right.

4. Point your eyes way down and way over to the left.

5. Whirl your eyes around in a circle.

6. Whirl your eyes around in the opposite direction.

7. Rest your eyes, and hum any tune—more than just one note (for about five seconds).

8. Count aloud to five.

9. Hum again (It is important to repeat this).

Summary of the Steps

Steps are listed in order. Refer to the headings below for specific negative emotions to select the appropriate major holon sequences. The nine-gamut sequence is the same for all algorithms.

1. Say out loud, "I want to be over ... (the specific symptom or negative emotion)."

2. Tap fifteen times on the karate point (side of the hand). Then, tap fifteen times under your nose (between the nose and the upper lip).

3. Repeat out loud, "I want to be over ... (the specific symptom or negative emotion)."

4. Tap the first *major holon* sequence (the tapping points in the order listed).

5. Do the nine-gamut sequence.

6. Again, tap the first *major holon* sequence (the tapping points in the order listed).

7. Tap any additional major holon sequence listed; then, do the nine-gamut sequence; then, again tap the additional major holon sequence. If there is only one major holon sequence, go on to the next step.

8. Say out loud, "I want to be *completely* over ... (the specific symptom or negative emotion)."

9. Tap fifteen times on the karate point (side of the hand). Then, tap fifteen times under your nose (between the nose and the upper lip).

10. Repeat out loud, "I want to be *completely* over . . . (the specific symptom or negative emotion)."

11. Repeat tapping the first *major holon* sequence (the tapping points in the order listed).

12. Repeat the nine-gamut sequence.

13. Repeat tapping the first *major holon* sequence (the tapping points in the order listed).

14. Repeat tapping any additional major holon sequence listed; then, do the nine-gamut sequence; then, again tap the additional major holon sequence. If there is only one major holon sequence, go on to the next step.

15. Say out loud, "I *will be completely* over . . . (the specific symptom or negative emotion)."

16. Tap fifteen times on the karate point (side of the hand). Then, tap fifteen times under your nose (between the nose and the upper lip).

17. Repeat tapping the first *major holon* sequence (the tapping points in the order listed).

18. Repeat the nine-gamut sequence.

19. Repeat tapping the first *major holon* sequence (the tapping points in the order listed).

20. Repeat tapping any additional major holon sequence listed; then, do the nine-gamut sequence; then, again tap the additional major holon sequence.

Holon Major Sequences

Refer to the steps listed above. Remember to make the appropriate statements, tap on the karate point and under the nose, and sandwich the nine-gamut treatment in between repetition of the major holon sequences. The nine-gamut sequence is abbreviated as 9GSQ, which means: do the nine gamut, then repeat the major holon sequence you did right before the nine-gamut.

Anxiety (simple)

- Eye, arm, collar, 9GSQ

Anxiety (complex)

- Eye, eyebrow, eye, eyebrow, arm, collar, 9GSQ
- Arm, eye, arm, collar, eyebrow, collar, eye, eyebrow, arm, collar, 9GSQ

Cravings

- Eye, collar, arm, collar, 9GSQ

Fear (general)

- Eye, eyebrow, eye, collar, arm, collar, eye, 9GSQ

Fear (phobic)

- Eye, arm, middle finger, eye, collar, under nose, eyebrow, eye, middle finger, eyebrow, index finger, eye, arm, middle finger, collar, middle finger, arm, collar, eye, collar, 9GSQ
- Eye, collar, eyebrow, tiny finger, eye, middle finger, collar, tiny finger, collar, middle finger, eyebrow, collar, index finger, collar, 9GSQ

Depression

- G50, collar, eyebrow, tiny finger, eye, arm, temple, eye, arm, collar, 9GSQ
- G50, eye, eyebrow, eye, tiny finger, eye, collar, index finger, eye, tiny finger, arm, collar, 9GSQ
- Eyebrow, middle finger, tiny finger, eye, temple, arm, collar, G50, eye, 9GSQ

Trauma (simple)

- Eyebrow, eye, eyebrow, temple, collar, eyebrow, eye, tiny finger, eye, temple, arm, collar, G50, eyebrow, 9GSQ

Trauma (complex, with abuse and self-criticism)

- Eye, arm, under nose, G50, eyebrow, eye, tiny finger, temple, arm, collar, eye, eyebrow, eye, G50, 9GSQ
- Eye, G50, middle finger, tiny finger, eyebrow, 9GSQ
- Index finger, collar, arm, index finger, eyebrow, eye, under nose, middle finger, tiny finger, eye, collar, 9GSQ
- G50, eyebrow, middle finger, tiny finger, temple, arm, collar, eye, eyebrow, index finger, temple, tiny finger, eye, eyebrow, 9GSQ
- G50, eye, eyebrow, index finger, middle finger, collar, eye, temple, eye, index finger, eye, eyebrow, tiny finger, 9GSQ (nine-gamut, then repeat major sequence)
- Eye, G50, index finger, middle finger, arm, eye, index finger, collar, eyebrow, G50, tiny finger, collar, index finger, eyebrow, eye, collar, 9GSQ
- Eye, temple, arm, middle finger, temple, index finger, G50, eye, tiny finger, collar, arm, collar, eye, 9GSQ
- Temple, eyebrow, G50, index finger, tiny finger, collar, arm, index finger, under nose, middle finger, G50, eyebrow, under nose, temple, arm, eye, index finger, middle finger, tiny finger, under nose, G50, eyebrow, 9GSQ
- Index finger, eye, eyebrow, G50, middle finger, central vessel, eye, G50, 9GSQ

Anger

- Eyebrow, tiny finger, eye, arm, temple, eye, arm, collar, tiny finger, collar, 9GSQ

Hurt

- Eyebrow, G50, eyebrow, collar, eye, arm, collar, tiny finger, eye, arm, collar, G50, collar, 9GSQ

Feeling overwhelmed

- Eye, arm, eyebrow, eye, eyebrow, arm, eyebrow, tiny finger, middle finger, collar, 9GSQ

Guilt

- Eye, arm, under nose, G50, eyebrow, eye, tiny finger, temple, arm, collar, eye, eyebrow, eye, G50, 9GSQ

Forgiveness

- Eye, arm, tiny finger, temple, eyebrow, eye, eyebrow, under nose, tiny finger, G50, temple, arm, collar, eye, eyebrow, collar, 9GSQ

Embarrassment

- Eye, arm, eyebrow, eye, eyebrow, eye, arm, collar, 9GSQ

Worry

- Eye, eyebrow, eye, collar, arm, collar, eye, collar, arm, collar, 9GSQ
- Eye, arm, collar, eye, 9GSQ

Irritation and Impatience

- Eye, eyebrow, middle finger, tiny finger, eye, collar, arm, eye, 9GSQ
- Eye, G50, index finger, eye, G50, eyebrow, tiny finger, eyebrow, 9GSQ
- Eye, G50, eyebrow, middle finger, temple, index finger, middle finger, 9GSQ

Stress

- Eye, eyebrow, arm, collar, 9GSQ
- Arm, eye, arm, collar, eyebrow, collar, eye, eyebrow, arm, collar, 9GSQ

Grief

- Eye, arm, under nose, G50, eyebrow, eye, tiny finger, temple, arm, collar, eye, eyebrow, eye, G50, 9GSQ
- G50, eyebrow, middle finger, tiny finger, temple, arm, collar, eye, eyebrow, index finger, temple, tiny finger, eye, eyebrow, 9GSQ
- Eye, G50, middle finger, tiny finger, eyebrow, 9GSQ
- G50, eye, eyebrow, index finger, middle finger, collar, eye, temple, eye, index finger, eye, eyebrow, tiny finger, 9GSQ (nine-gamut, then repeat major sequence)
- Eye, G50, index finger, middle finger, arm, eye, index finger, collar, eyebrow, G50, tiny finger, collar, index finger, eyebrow, eye, collar, 9GSQ

Love pain and rejection

- Eyebrow, G50, eyebrow, collar, eye, arm, collar, tiny finger, eye, arm, collar, G50, collar, 9GSQ
- G50, eye, eyebrow, eye, tiny finger, eye, collar, index finger, eye, tiny finger, arm, collar, 9GSQ
- Eyebrow, eye, eyebrow, temple, collar, eyebrow, eye, tiny finger, eye, temple, arm, collar, G50, eyebrow, 9GSQ
- Eye, arm, under nose, G50, eyebrow, eye, tiny finger, temple, arm, collar, eye, eyebrow, eye, G50, 9GSQ

Procrastination

- Eye, arm, eye, collar, eyebrow, eye, middle finger, eyebrow, index finger, eye, arm, middle finger, tiny finger, collar, middle finger, arm, collar, 9GSQ
- Eye, collar, eyebrow, tiny finger, eye, middle finger, collar, tiny finger, collar, middle finger, eyebrow, collar, index finger, collar, 9GSQ

Acknowledgments

Though I am a reporter, practitioner, and enthusiastic proponent of the methods and attitudes I described in *Overcome Anxiety*, the subject's foundation resides in the brilliance and tireless work of those who discovered and developed these healing techniques over decades.

Accordingly, I respectfully acknowledge the work of the late Dr. Roger Callahan and his wife, Joanne Callahan. As a team, they pioneered the advent and practice of Thought Field Therapy, currently practiced by thousands of practitioners worldwide. The Callahans taught many professionals how to use TFT successfully to heal and eliminate a wide range of debilitating problems. Dr. Callahan mentored me for decades, generously offering his time and expertise, taking personal interest, and adhering to meticulous, scientific, and maverick methodology. In his scientific approach and dedication to patients, he braved skepticism, ridicule, and dismissal, never veering from the truths he applied for human betterment. The Callahans changed my life, personally and professionally, and embellished my skills and ability to change the lives of thousands of others.

My professional practice and personal well-being changed dramatically and gradually when I met Dr. Siegfried Othmer and decided to try his methods of brain training. He has been my mentor for over thirty years. I am indebted to him and his late wife, Susan Othmer, for their pioneering work with technology, neurobiology, and the mysteries of the human mind. Their teaching, support, and technological advances have proliferated through me and many other professionals to improve the lives, health, and satisfaction of many thousands of people. We are just at the beginning of a revolution in health care.

I also want to thank Kurt Othmer for his masterful administration of the business side of operations in sustaining the EEG Institute that supports practitioners with equipment, technical issues, ongoing software development, research, and education.

I thank my editor, Marly Cornell, who meticulously refined my message and my style with tactful and direct suggestions and critiques.

I pay tribute to my wife, Giulia, a talented photographer, graphic design artist, and fashion designer. She has encouraged me in its writing, served as a sounding board for my ideas and prose, criticized my aesthetic departures, and been consistently tolerant of my passionate and often isolated relationship with writing. Thank you, darling, for your support and love and for renewing my spirit daily to one of eagerness instead of anxiety.

About the Author

Dr. Mark Steinberg is a licensed psychologist with expertise in clinical, educational, and neuropsychology. Throughout a practice spanning four decades, Dr. Steinberg has administered more than 100,000 evaluation and treatment procedures, treating children, adolescents, and adults. He offers a range of services dealing with attention and mood disorders, behavior problems, family and communication issues, developmental disabilities, educational and learning problems, parenting challenges, habit change, addictions, and neurological disorders (including headaches, seizures, and sleep disorders).

By blending the latest technological advances with traditional and scientific methods, Dr. Steinberg improves functioning and eliminates problems that have often persisted for years. He is well-known for his pioneering work with EEG neurofeedback and voice technology, treatment that eliminates negative emotions in minutes.

Widely consulted as a medical expert, and the winner of local and statewide awards, Dr. Steinberg has made many appearances on local and national television, offering psychological expertise on topics pertaining to health, behavior, and how to live a more satisfying and productive life.

Dr. Steinberg offers individual services, seminars, and trainings.
For more information:
Call (408) 356-1002
Visit **www.marksteinberg.com**

Other books by Mark Steinberg, PhD

Life Control: Take Charge and Get Ahead

Reality Reports: Essays on Mental, Emotional, Spiritual, and Social Issues in the Twenty-First Century

Living Intact: Challenge and Choice in Tough Times

When God Takes Away: Living with Loss and Surrender

Confessions of a Maverick Mind: A Psychologist Shares Stories and Adventures, Essays and Articles, and Poems and Songs

Staying Madly in Love with Your Spouse: Guide to a Happier Marriage; and *Living Intact: Challenge and Choice in Tough Times.*

ADD: The 20-Hour Solution, coauthored with Siegfried Othmer, PhD

Made in the USA
Las Vegas, NV
10 December 2023

82486770R00152